Tales — Heroes, Deeds, and Wonders

Ron Benson

Lynn Bryan

Kim Newlove

Charolette Player

Liz Stenson

CONSULTANTS

Susan Elliott

Diane Lomond

Ken MacInnis

Elizabeth Parchment

Prentice Hall Ginn Canada
Scarborough, Ontario

Contents

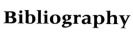

 Selections with this symbol are available on audio.

 This symbol indicates student writing.

Canadian selections are marked with this symbol.

Messages in Myths

by Sharon Stewart
Illustrated by Normand Cousineau

Thor the Thunderer. Maui the Great. Athena the Wise. All over the world, people tell stories about the mighty deeds of gods and heroes like these. Such stories are called myths—but what, really, is a myth?

Our English word "myth" comes from the ancient Greek word *mythos*, which means "a spoken or written story." Myths aren't just any stories, though. They may be entertaining, but they also carry messages. Unlike legends, which often have some link to historical fact, myths belong to the timeless world of "once-was-and-always-is." They are stories that try to answer questions people have asked themselves from the beginning of time: What is the nature of the world? Where did people come from? What should I do to live a good life?

Creation Myths

Around the world, myths give many different explanations of how the world was created. Ancient Egyptian myths tell how Nun, the Sleeping Ocean, was surrounded by Chaos. From Nun was born Ra-Atum, the Complete One, who created the world as we know it. On the west coast of North America, Haida myths tell how Raven was thrown out of heaven and made land rise from the sea by flapping his wings. In Japanese myth, the god Izanagi and the goddess Izanami brought land up out of the sea by stirring it with a spear.

How, then, did people come to be? A myth from Papua-New Guinea says that Kambel, the sky god, heard voices inside a great tree trunk and opened it, releasing the first people. In Peruvian myth, the Creator god Viracocha first modelled human beings out of stone, and painted them just as they would appear in life—

men, women, and children. A Yoruba myth from Africa tells how the first people were formed out of clay before Olorun, the Creator, breathed life into them.

Where did other living things come from? A myth of the Aboriginal People of Australia tells how Yulunggur, the Rainbow Serpent, came to Earth and went on a rampage. He scared the first people so badly that some stood stock-still and turned into trees. Others hid under rocks and became tortoises, or bounded off as kangaroos, or fluttered away as birds. As Yulunggur thrashed about on the ground, he shaped the landscape into hills and valleys, then he rose into the sky again where he can still be seen as the rainbow.

Myths That Explain the Nature of the World

Many myths explain natural events in beautiful and powerful ways. A Siberian myth explains day and night by telling how a giant elk captures the sun each day and carries it off in its antlers. In the old Norse myths of Scandinavia, Thor's mighty hammer caused lightning, and the rumbling of his chariot was thunder. In North America, the Kiowa People told how tornadoes came from the flapping of the wings of a giant sky horse.

Other myths are "why" stories that explain animal characteristics. For example, a myth of the Galla People in Ethiopia tells how the Maker once wished to give a gift to human beings. He sent them the power to exchange their old skins for new youthful ones, but a snake

got the present by mistake. To this day, all snakes can shed their skins, but people can't.

Myths That Explain Folkways

Other myths give specific information about the culture in which they are told. Some explain how a particular people came to live in a particular place. For instance, a Tukano myth from the Amazon explains how Pahmuri-Mahse brought people up the Amazon River in a canoe shaped like a giant anaconda snake. Wherever the canoe stopped along the way, communities of the Tukano People settled down.

Other myths explain how human beings got the different foods they eat. One Iroquois myth tells how a warrior named Two-Feather met a mysterious green-skinned woman with silky golden hair, and was given the gift of corn to share with his people. In Japan, myths tell of Uke Mochi, the food goddess, from whose body came rice, corn, and beans. In Greece, it was the goddess Demeter who taught people how to gather kernels of wild wheat and plant them to produce crops. In Bali, Wisnu, the water god, forces the Lord of Heaven to teach people how to sow, care for, and harvest rice.

Myths That Teach Lessons

Myths also teach values. Sometimes they deal with good and evil. In ancient Persian myth, the good spirit Ahura Mazda must struggle forever against the evil Angra Mainyu, for both good and evil are part of the world. Norse myths say that evil can never be completely removed from the world. In the shape of the great wolf Fenris, it lies bound until the final day when the gods will battle the giants and the world as we know it will end.

Myths can also teach more personal values. A myth of the Bella Coola People tells how Eagle Man punished the cruelty and selfishness of certain villagers by dropping them into the sea where they became the islands of the Pacific Coast. A myth from Nigeria tells how the sky once was close above the ground and provided a delicious and plentiful food. When people grew greedy and wasted it, the sky moved far away. Ever since, people have had to grow their own food and learn not to waste it.

Laziness is often punished in myths. When the people of Thebes, in ancient Greece, became lazy and didn't make proper sacrifices, the god Apollo punished them by sending an evil creature called the Sphinx. The Sphinx asked a riddle of all passersby and destroyed them when they couldn't answer. The Anishinabe People of North America tell how maple trees once gave pure syrup all year round until the people became so lazy that they did no work at all. So Gitchee Manitou, the Creator, made the sap in the maple tree thin. Now people have to work hard to get their maple syrup. The sap only flows once a year, too!

Myths often teach generosity and self-sacrifice. One myth from India tells how a prince saved a dove from an eagle by cutting off bits of his own flesh to feed the hungry eagle. Pleased by his virtue, the gods healed him and blessed him. A myth from Sri Lanka tells of a Hare who sacrificed its life to feed a holy man and was rewarded by going to live on the moon where you can see it still.

Respect for the natural world and the balance of nature is another value taught in myths. A Cheyenne story warns of a great beaver that gnaws at the Tree of the World, which it will someday bring down. When the balance of the world is upset, the beaver gnaws faster. So it's wise not to annoy that beaver!

Myths About Heroes

Myths also teach values through the adventures of heroes who perform great deeds or undertake difficult quests. These heroes are often the children of the gods and many have special powers. Though brave, many heroes are not wise, and they always pay for their mistakes.

Yi was a mighty Chinese archer. He had once been a god, but lived on Earth as a mortal hero. Yi became very much afraid of death though. So after many heroic deeds, he demanded and got from the gods a potion to let him live forever. Things didn't work out as he planned, however, because Chang-Er, his wife, couldn't resist drinking the potion. She flew away to the moon and Yi was left lamenting.

Another unfortunate hero was Achilles, a famous Greek warrior who fought at the siege of Troy. Proud of his great deeds, he quarrelled with Agamemnon, the Greek king. Then he sulked in his tent, refusing to fight, and the Greeks began to lose the war. Achilles' best friend pleaded with him, then stole his armor and went out to fight in his place. He was killed. Too late, Achilles repented. He defeated the warrior who had slain his friend, but soon after, the warrior's brother shot him with a poisoned arrow and Achilles died.

Do Myths Matter?

Myths are wonderful stories and people all over the world have listened to them for thousands of years. The messages they carry still matter today because many myths around the world have similar themes. Maybe that's because people are amazingly similar across time and space. So, a myth is like a telescope that lets us see distant times and places in order to understand them better. It's also like a microscope that helps us put our own values into focus. The real magic of myths is that in telling us about other peoples, they tell us most of all about ourselves.

Helpers of Humanity

Written and Illustrated by Song Nan Zhang

According to Chinese myth, five emperors ruled the heavens. The Central Emperor was associated with yellow earth; the Southern Emperor controlled fire and summer; the Eastern Emperor controlled spring; the Western Emperor controlled autumn; the Northern Emperor controlled winter. These great rulers and other lesser gods watched over life on Earth, and sometimes acted to help human beings.

Youchao and the First Dwellings

From the time they were created, people loved daylight, for they could hunt and forage for food and see any danger ahead. But they were frightened at night.

In the dark, strange noises disturbed their sleep and wild beasts sometimes came out of the forest to attack them.

Caves offered refuge, but these were so cold in winter some people froze, and so damp the rest of the year they were often sick.

One god did not like seeing people suffer. He came down to Earth to see what he could do. One day as he sat under a tree wondering how he could help, he looked up and saw birds building a nest. Why don't I, he thought, teach people how to build nests for themselves?

The birds used a tree branch to hold their nest steady, so he used wood for a frame to hold up his dwelling. The birds used dry grass to weave their nest; he covered his frame with hay.

He liked the result, so he taught people how to build shelters where they could be safe, warm, and comfortable.

The people were so happy in their new homes, they honored the god by calling him Youchao, which means "Having Nest."

Shennong Shows How to Grow Food

Gods never suffer from hunger, but human beings must spend most of their time searching for food. Animals and fish were easy to find in summer, but difficult in winter, and many people died of starvation.

The Southern Emperor decided to help. It would be easier if people could live off plants that they could raise near their homes and store for the winter. He could teach them how to cultivate plants, but there was a more serious problem.

Among the millions of plants, which were safe to eat and which were poisonous?

The Southern Emperor set out on a tour of Earth, determined to taste every plant and make a list of those that were good to eat. It was slow work, so he invented a magic whip to help him. The whip could tell the qualities of a plant just by touching it. He also brought grains down from heaven and taught people how to plow, sow, and harvest.

People honored the Southern Emperor by calling him Shennong, or "the Peasant God."

The Central Emperor was so moved by what the Southern Emperor had done that he added a gift of his own, the nine-tasselled golden wheat. It would result in many golden harvests and provide food that could be stored through the winter.

Suiren Makes Fire

To the early humans, fire was dangerous and fascinating.

When lightning set fire to dry wood in the forest, it was terrifying. Animals and people who could not run from it died. But when the fire burned itself out, people found the ashes warmed them and roasted food. They saw that fire could be useful.

If only they could start a fire when they wanted to and control it.

Near the edge of the earth was a place that neither sunshine nor moonlight could reach. The only light came from a giant tree that sent out sparkles.

One day a travelling god walked by the tree and sat down to sleep. He was awakened by the sound of a nighthawk pecking at a branch above him. Every time the bird pecked, sparks came from the tree, dropped to the ground, and set fire to any dry leaves they touched.

If human beings had bits of the tree, the god realized, they could make fire whenever and wherever they wanted. He cut branches from it and taught people to drill on the dry wood and make sparks to start a fire.

The tree was called Flint because of the sparks it gave out, and the people, in gratitude to the god, called him Suiren, or "Mr. Flint."

Fushi Explains the Universe

Fushi, the Eastern Emperor, did a lot to help people. He taught them how to make strings for their bows so they could hunt and how to knit nets so they could fish. He even invented a musical instrument, a pipe made of bamboo, so they would have entertainment.

He was very ambitious. He wanted to understand and explain the laws that ruled the universe. That would be the greatest gift he could give humankind.

For years he meditated. Every morning he sat upon his altar, listened to the tiniest sound coming from the earth, and thought about it. Finally, he decided that he had found the secret of existence.

He drew up a map to explain it. The circle in the centre, resembling an egg, is Taichi, the beginning of the universe. The black and white halves, or *Yin* and *Yang*, stand for the female and male forces that control human existence. They join head to tail like a pair of fish. All life, every human being, has both *Yin* and *Yang* within. Happiness depends on their being in perfect balance.

The eight symbols around the Taichi are called *Ba Gua*. Each is a different combination of long lines, the *Yang*, and short lines, the *Yin*. Each symbol stands for one part of the laws that control the universe, telling us what has happened in history and what will happen in the future.

Fushi's map remains to this day a mystery, fascinating and challenging to mathematicians, scientists, and philosophers around the world.

Nuwa Mends the Sky

The earth was a peaceful place. Human beings were in harmony with each other and learning to do many things better.

But one day a terrible disaster struck. The dome-shaped sky split open and endless rain poured down, flooding the earth. People and animals were swept away. A few survivors managed to get to the mountaintops, but there they were threatened by volcanoes erupting and hungry animals desperate for food.

The goddess Nuwa was horrified as she saw the people she had created being destroyed. She went to work to mend the sky.

She collected many five-colored stones and, using fire from heaven, she melted them down into hot lava. This she used to mend the cracks in the sky. She then sacrificed the great heavenly tortoise and used its legs to hold up the four corners of the sky.

When the sky was mended, she stopped the floods by creating lakes and dams out of ashes and earth.

At last the disaster was over, the earth was safe, and all living things were at peace. Even the animals, birds, and snakes no longer used their teeth, claws, or stings to hurt, but lived off plants.

Nuwa rode her winged dragon back to her heavenly home. She told the Yellow Emperor she wanted no honors for saving human life on Earth, asked him to look after people in the future, and disappeared.

The inhabitants of Earth never saw her again, but they ignored her request not to be honored and built giant statues and magnificent temples in her name.

The Birth of the Alphabet

While the Emperor Fushi was working out his laws of the universe, a minor god called Cangjie came up with an important invention.

He was in charge of historical records. He kept an account of everything that happened by tying thousands of knots on thousands of ropes every day. He had two extra eyes to help, but the work was still slow. He decided there must be a better way to keep records than using ropes.

One day, weary of work, he went for a walk. As he looked down at the ground in front of him, he saw a trail of animal footprints and got an idea. If people could look at footprints and know which animal had made them, why could they not look at picture-signs and know what they stood for?

He began to make simple drawings of everything he saw around him. He made thousands of sketches and made sure that people understood them. This was the beginning of the Chinese alphabet. Now they would be able to write letters to people far away, record history, and pass stories on to future generations.

As the years passed, Cangjie's drawings became simpler and easier to

copy. Although to this day many of the Chinese characters resemble the original drawings, most have to be learned one by one. It's hard work for Chinese children learning to read, but it means that people of the many different languages used throughout China can all understand what is written.

A B O U T   T H E

A U T H O R   SONG NAN ZHANG

Song Nan Zhang was born in Shanghai, China in 1942. He received his Master's Degree from the Central Institute of Fine Arts of China. In 1984 and 1985 he travelled abroad and studied at L'Ecole des Beaux Arts in Paris. He returned to China to become the assistant director and, later, an associate professor at the Institute where he had studied. Over the years, Song travelled to Canada several times and in December of 1991, he became a permanent resident of Canada.

The Creation

An Iroquois Myth

by Joseph Bruchac
Illustrated by Sylvie Bourbonnière

Before this world came to be,
there lived in the Sky-World
an ancient chief.
In the centre of his land
grew a beautiful tree
which had four white roots
stretching to each
of the four directions:
North, South, East, and West.
From that beautiful tree,
all good things grew.

Then it came to be
that the beautiful tree
was uprooted and through
the hole it made in the Sky-World
fell the youthful wife
of the ancient chief,
a handful of seeds,
which she grabbed from the tree
as she fell, clutched in her hand.

Far below there were only water
and water creatures
who looked up as they swam.

"Someone comes," said the duck.
"We must make room for her."

The great turtle swam up
from his place in the depths.
"There is room on my back,"
the great turtle said.

"But there must be earth
where she can stand," said the duck
and so he dove beneath the waters,
but he could not reach the bottom.

"I shall bring up earth,"
the loon then said and he dove too,
but could not reach the bottom.

"I shall try," said the beaver
and he too dove but
could not reach the bottom.

Finally the muskrat tried.
He dove as deeply as he could,
swimming until his lungs almost burst.
With one paw he touched the bottom,
and came up with a tiny speck
of earth clutched in his paw.

"Place the earth on my back,"
the great turtle said,
and as they spread
the tiny speck of earth it grew
larger and larger and larger
until it became the whole world.

Then two swans flew up
and between their wings
they caught the woman
who fell from the sky.
They brought her gently
down to the earth
where she dropped her handful
of seeds from the Sky-World.

Then it was that the first plants grew
and life on this new earth began.

The River that Went to the Sky

by Kasiya Makaka Phiri
Illustrated by Kasia Charko

nce there was a River. It ran from one side of the great continent to the other, and it was so wide it looked like a lake, and the land around it was rich. All the animals that lived there had plenty of everything—grass to graze, fruit to eat, nuts to crack, roots to chew, bark to nibble, and leaves to eat. The animals ambled all day long, eating a little, stopping, gazing into the distance, eating a little more, and going on slowly, for there was no hurry. The great vast River meandered across the land, avoiding all the mountains, choosing only the plains and the valleys, but always spreading wide, wide across the land. It rolled gently from one side of the vast continent and went to sleep and glided on the night tide to the other side. Backward and forward. It felt good and made happy noises on the banks, like the sound of calabashes filling with water, one gulp at a time.

On the banks, grew the low grasses that like to trail their roots in cool river water. With them grew the papyrus and bulrushes. Behind them grew those grasses that like to smell the water every day and hear the happy sounds of the River. Water trees stood knee-deep in the water, looking toward the grasses of the low plains that gave way to ankle-high grass, then knee-high grass, all the way to the towering elephant grass. Then came the tall trees of the woods, beyond which were the high plains and foothills of great mountains. The high plains were covered in shorter grasses where the swift wind blew, keeping everything down except in the sheltered folds of the rolling ridges. In these hidden valleys were groves of rare trees and flowers and many other plants.

So everything was all right, until one day the River, gliding sleepily, looked up and saw the stars in the night sky.

"What is that?" said the River in a sleepy voice.

Hyena, who happened to be nearby taking a sip of water, looked up and said, "What's what, where?"

"Up there with the many eyes," said the sleepy River.

"That is the night sky," Hyena said and went on his way.

"Oh, how I wish I could go to the sky," said the River, sighing as it fell asleep.

The grass with the roots in the water heard this and whispered: "The River wants to go to the sky."

The whisper went on, to the papyrus, to the reeds, to the short plain grass, and to the knee-high grass.

"The River wants to go to the sky!"

"The River . . ."

". . . wants to . . ."

". . . go to . . ."

". . . the sky. . . ."

The whisper went very fast until it was at the edge of the woods that are hedged by bushes guarding the foothills of the great mountains and the high plains.

"The River wants to go to the sky," said a bush, and the trees whispered from trunk to branch to leaf to leaf to leaf like a gentle stir in an invisible breeze all the way to the wind-swept high plains where the grass lay low below the swift wind.

The wind was quick at picking up whispers from the lower plains, so it snapped the whisper up and dragged it over the high plains up to the mountains and over the peaks where nothing grew because it was too cold. Away into the sky the wind carried the whisper.

"Shoosh-whoosh, whoosh-whoosh, the River wants to go to the sky."

The night sky heard it, the stars heard it, and early the following day before dawn, just as it was eating its breakfast ready to start the day, the Sun heard it.

"Very well, I'll visit the River today," said the Sun.

The River woke up very early, and soon after, the Sun came to visit.

"I hear you want to go to the sky, meandering River?" said the Sun.

"Yes! Oh, to walk the blue and see the twinkling eyes," the River sighed.

"Very well," said the Sun. "I can help you up, but you'll have to find your way down."

"Down! It looks so beautiful up there, I won't want to find my way down."

Gazelle, who happened to be taking a drink just then, sprang up and ran to Elephant and said, "The Sun is going to take the great River up to the sky, and she says she'll never come back here again!"

Elephant thought for a while, then raised her trunk and blew a message into the air. The wind, who was always quick at picking up messages, snapped it up and everywhere it blew, the animals and the plants heard it.

The trees were the first to react. They gathered together into the densest forest ever and talked over the matter for days and days. The gathering of trees and creepers became a jungle, but the grasses, thinking it was too dark under the eaves of those huge trees, wandered out onto the plains, and they were so happy they rocked in the wind singing in their throaty voices. They spread as far as the eye could see. Some small thorn trees and bushes came out and dotted the grassy plains, and this became the savanna.

When the animals gathered, they too talked for days and days.

"This is a serious matter," said Elephant.

"It is time to migrate to faraway places," said Rhino. Saying so, he put down his head and followed his nose South. South, South, always South.

That started the exodus and animals wandered in all directions. Great Gorilla and Brainy Chimpanzee, feeling that they did not want to go too far, simply went into the jungle. Tree Pangolin, Leopard, Gabon Viper, and Royal Antelope did the same.

Elephant led a whole delegation South following the rhinoceros. Buffalo, Lion, Giraffe, Gazelle, Hyena, Zebra, Cheetah, and many others wandered South and roamed the grasslands. But rock-climbing Barbary Sheep, Camel, Addax, Sand Cat, Desert Hedgehog, Fennec Fox, Jerboa, Sand Grouse, and many others remained exactly where they were.

Meanwhile, the Sun had gathered all its strength. It sent its hottest rays to heat the River, and slowly, oh so slowly, you could not see what was happening, the River started to lift in particles too tiny for the eye to see. Up, up, up they went until they were so high that it felt cold. Then the tiny particles of the River huddled together and formed white fluffy clouds of all sizes. They were so happy to be floating in the air, and they waited in excitement for the spectacle of the night sky when they would walk among the many winking stars.

Sure enough, in the evening, the night sky prepared to lay out the best winking stars for the visiting clouds to walk among, and as it got darker, the stars winked and twinkled and sparkled.

"Oh, isn't this wonderful!" said a cloud. "Simply stupendous!"

Whoosh! A gust of wind came in.

"You're sitting on my bit of sky ledge," the wind said.

"Oh, I beg your pardon," said the cloud, and she moved over to one side.

Whoosh! Gusts of wind came over and over again, here and everywhere. They claimed parts of the sky where the clouds were. Sometimes they came while the clouds were trying to get some sleep, and they would shake them awake and push them over.

Now, pushing and shoving is about the only thing that the gentle River would not stand. And all the clouds remembered the peaceful days of being water down on Earth. They remembered the gentle flow in one direction and the gliding back on the tide, and a small cloud said, "I want to go home."

Yes. They all wanted to go home. But how? The wind, so quick at picking up conversations, snapped up the news of the clouds trying to go home, and it gathered all its sisters, cousins, and brothers.

WWHHOOOSSSHH!!

They carried the clouds high and made them feel colder, and as the clouds huddled together, they grew heavy and began to fall as rain. Down below, the Sun was still burning out any manner of moisture that remained in the river bed.

But it rained. It rained all day long and all night long. It rained everywhere, but never in the old river bed. It rained in Abyssinia and formed the Blue Nile. It rained and rained and formed the White Nile and Lake Victoria and Lake Tanganyika and Lake Malawi and Lake Chad, Lake Turkana, and many small lakes besides. It rained and rained and formed the Shire River. It rained and formed the Zambezi. It rained some more and the Limpopo, the Orange, the Niger, the Luangwa, and many, many other rivers were born. It rained heavily and lightly, day and night, and if you put your hands over your ears and moved them on and off, you could hear something like a song, but not quite a song. Something like words, but not quite like words:

"I am the River, the River that went to the sky for a walk.
I am the River, the River that went to the sky for a walk."

It rained and rained everywhere, but never in the place where the River once lived. If any of the drops ventured anywhere near that place, the Sun bore down on them and sent them back into the sky. And it is true. If you go to the great continent of Africa today, you will see the vast expanse of sand where the meandering River lived. Sand everywhere, even in places where grass had been plenty. To this day, the wildebeest have not stopped running away from the Sun, following their noses to wetter places where the grass would be as it used to be once upon a time, a long time ago, on the great continent of Africa.

ABOUT THE AUTHOR   KASIYA MAKAKA PHIRI

Born in Zimbabwe to Malawian parents, Kasiya Makaka Phiri was educated in Malawi. He later taught in schools and colleges there. He is a poet, playwright, and storyteller. He tells new stories and retells old ones first to his three daughters and then to audiences of all ages. Kasiya is currently studying African literature at the University of Wisconsin.

HOW LIGHTNING AND THUNDER GOT UP IN THE SKY

In the Caribbean, a long time ago, there was a young, mean little boy whose name was Lightning. He liked to tease his sister, Thunder. Every time Lightning teased Thunder, she would yell really loud at him from the top of her lungs! Now, Lightning had special powers—he could shoot out sparks of fire, heat, and electricity from all over his body. Sometimes he would terrorize the town and damage everything on purpose.

Finally, the villagers of the town had had enough. They arranged a meeting with the mayor about what to do with Lightning and Thunder.

"Lightning has set my barn on fire. Thunder scared away all my animals with her big loud voice," protested one of the villagers. Everyone agreed that something had to be done.

At the end of the meeting, the mayor decided that the best thing to do was to make Lightning and Thunder promise never to be mean or loud again. They would have to leave the village if they did not keep their promise.

Lightning and Thunder agreed, but they did not keep their word. Within days they became noisier and more harmful than ever before. Whenever Lightning did something bad, there was Thunder, shouting at her loudest.

That was it! The mayor gave them a serious talk. He and the townspeople warned them not to be bad, but again they didn't listen, so it was decided that they would have to leave the town forever.

The townspeople brought Lightning and Thunder to the top of the biggest hill and everybody started to whistle. Thunder and Lightning didn't know what was going on. The whistling continued until a gigantic flock of birds, of every kind, came swooping down from the sky. From toucans to budgies, they all swarmed around Thunder and Lightning and carried them up to the sky where they placed them on a cloud and left them there.

Every so often, Lightning does something bad and you can hear Ol' Thunder screaming and yelling at him from the top of her lungs. Sometimes Thunder yells too much and scares Lightning so he starts to cry. Sometimes he cries so much that his tears flood people's homes. If Lightning really gets upset, he sends some of his powers down to Earth. Then you can hear Thunder yelling her head off.

Have you ever heard Thunder yell or seen Lightning's powers? It's kind of pretty to watch.

Retold by Megan Small
Grade 6

I like to write stories because writing allows you to express your innermost ideas.

Who

by Richard Thompson
Illustrated by Martin Springett

If you go to the forest and try to call an owl by name—if, for instance, you call, "Bartholomew! Bartholomew! Are you there?" a voice may answer back. And that voice will say, "Whoooo?"

And that is because owls do not have names.

But there was a time, long ago, when owls called each other by name just as you and I do. In that time, there lived two owls named Bartholomew and Eleanor, and they had three children.

When their first child was born, they decided to name the hatchling Night. "Our daughter will grow to be a stealthy hunter," Bartholomew said. "We will name her Night, for no hunter steals through the forest more quietly than Night does."

The girl was called Night. And Night, the bringer of darkness, was pleased when he heard it. He sent the owlet a present—a night-dark cloak embroidered with stars.

When their second child was born, Bartholomew declared, "We will name this child Moon, for she will grow to be a great beauty, and in all the forest nothing can rival the radiant beauty of the Moon."

The girl was called Moon. And Moon who lives in the sky was flattered when she heard it. She sent the infant owl a present—a mirror of fragile crystal.

And in time a third child, a son, was born to Bartholomew and Eleanor. "This boy shall grow to great wisdom and will be the keeper of many secrets," Eleanor told their friends. "We shall name him Tomorrow after the greatest keeper of secrets."

And so the boy was called Tomorrow. And he who no one really knows was flattered when he heard it. He sent the child a present—a box with a golden lock and key in which to keep his secrets.

The owlets grew, in time, to owlhood. As they grew, the forest animals spoke of them in awed whispers.

"Beware of the owl called Night," warned Squirrel. "She hunts on silent wings."

"We are very beautiful with our painted wings," said Butterfly, "but not nearly as beautiful as the owl called Moon."

"I know many of the secrets of the forest," said Snake, "but no one knows what secrets the owl called Tomorrow has locked away in his box."

Sadly, the young owls believed all the wonderful things the other animals said about them…

Night Owl pulled her cloak around herself and spoke in dangerous whispers. "I am not only the stealthiest hunter in the forest, I am more stealthy even than Night, for whom I was named. The bringer of darkness always gives warning of his approach in the brilliant colors of the sunset. But no one knows when I am coming."

Moon Owl stroked her feathers and murmured, "I am not only the most beautiful

creature in the forest, I am more beautiful than Moon, for whom I was named. Her beauty dwindles night by night until she vanishes altogether, but my beauty is constant."

Tomorrow looked out at the forest from under hooded eyes and said softly, "I have secrets locked away that even Tomorrow, for whom I was named, will never share. And when Tomorrow gives away his secrets to Today, as he must, I will still have mine."

Echoes of the owls' boastful words reached Night, the bringer of darkness, and Moon, who lives in the sky, and Tomorrow, whom no one really knows. They were angry.

"These scamps shall learn a lesson," Night growled. Moon and Tomorrow agreed.

When Night next came to the forest, Moon stayed at home, even though she was at her fullest and most brilliant. Night turned his cloak inside out so no one could see the stars. The forest was inky dark. Even the keenest sighted animals could not see to move.

"Never mind," said all the animals, "everything will be fine when Tomorrow comes.

But Tomorrow didn't come.

The animals became very hungry and thirsty, but still they dared not venture out into the absolute darkness.

Finally, one brave mouse crept from her hole and, feeling her way carefully across the forest floor, made her way to the owls' tree. "Night Owl," she called, "the light has been hidden from us, but you can find it if any hunter can."

Night Owl crept out onto the branch in front of the nest and looked at the impenetrable darkness. The blackness filled her with a dread she had never felt before. She turned silently and slid back along the branch. As she went, her cloak caught on a twig and pulled from her shoulders. It fluttered down through the blackness and was never seen again.

"Moon Owl," called the mouse, "come and let your beauty light the forest."

The beautiful young owl crept out onto the branch in front of the nest. But her beauty and the mouse's simple homeliness were equally invisible in the great blackness. Moon Owl wondered if she had disappeared. As she lifted her mirror to check, it slipped from her grasp and shattered on the ground below the tree.

"Tomorrow Owl," called the mouse, "please come and use your wisdom to bring light to the forest."

Bartholomew and Eleanor's son dragged his box out of the nest and in the great blackness fumbled with the lock. The key slipped from his claws and fell to the forest floor. No one will ever know for sure if the young owl had a secret in that box that would have brought the light they sought, for the key was lost forever amongst the ferns.

The mouse began to cry softly. When Eleanor heard her tiny sobs, she said, "Bartholomew, you must speak to the bringer of darkness. Perhaps he will listen to you."

Bartholomew stepped carefully out onto the branch and called to Night, "My friend, why are you angry with us? Where is Moon? Why doesn't Tomorrow come?"

Night replied, "Bartholomew Owl, when you gave our names to your children, we were pleased and flattered. But your children have forgotten who they are. For all their stealth and beauty and wisdom, they are, after all, animals among animals, and they must remember that. We want our names back!"

"But what will we call our children?" cried Bartholomew.

"That is your problem," said Night. "If you want Moon and Tomorrow to return to the forest, you will give us our names back."

Fortunately, Night could not see the anger that flashed in Bartholomew's eyes, nor hear the protest that shouted in his heart. And Bartholomew, being somewhat wiser than his children, answered as he knew he must.

"It will be done."

Reluctantly, Bartholomew told his children they had to give back their wonderful names. And, reluctantly, they did.

Tomorrow came to the forest and the animals could see to hunt for food and water. When Night came again, Moon came with him. And all was as it should be again.

But Bartholomew did not share in the rejoicing that filled the forest. His children had been robbed to ransom the light, and, though he had no choice but to pay the ransom, he was determined that the sacrifice should be remembered.

"If my children cannot have the names they deserve," he declared, "they shall have no names at all."

And that is why, to this very day, owls do not have names.

So if you go into the forest and try to call an owl by name…

ABOUT THE AUTHOR

RICHARD THOMPSON

Richard Thompson lives with his wife Maggee and daughter Jesse in Prince George, British Columbia. He began storytelling when he was a pre-school teacher and he later became a successful author with the publication of his series of *Jesse* stories. He has also published several picture books, an illustrated collection of bedtime stories, a novel for older children, and two collections of "draw and tell" stories. Soon after he began writing, Richard started professional storytelling and now makes many public appearances and readings.

The Beasts of Never

Illustrated by Hélène Bouliane

Bunyip
by Jenny Wagner

"What do bunyips look like?"
  asked the bunyip.
"Horrible," said the wallaby.
  "They have webbed feet and
  feathers."
"Fine handsome feathers," said the
  bunyip hopefully.
"Horrible feathers," said the wallaby
  firmly . . .
"Handsome webbed feet?" called
  the bunyip, but there was no
  answer.

"Can you please tell me what
  bunyips look like?"
"Yes," said the man. . . . "Bunyips
  don't look like anything. . . .
Bunyips simply don't exist."
The bunyip was shaken. . . .
"What a pity," he murmured.
"What a pity, what a pity."

Cerberus
by N.B. Taylor

There!
That terrible three-necked
hound
Cerberus crouched. . .
Baying savagely from
his triple throat . . .
he barred the way to Pluto's house.

he Griffin
by Arnold Sundgaard

Protector of Pharaohs,
Defender of Kings,
The Griffin watched over
Their Crowns and their Rings,
With Wings of an Eagle,
And sharp Lion claws,
It once tore to pieces
The Breaker of Laws.
It heard every whisper,
And knew every plot
And you may believe it,
Or else you may not!

he Manticore
by Jeanne Steig

A mythic beast, the manticore—
Dragon behind and man before,
With lion sandwiched in between 'em.
No living soul has ever seen him,
Nor any combination of
The creatures in the list above.

Pegasus
by Eleanor Farjeon

He could not be captured,
He could not be bought,
His running was rhythm,
His standing was thought;
With one eye on sorrow
And one eye on mirth,
He galloped in heaven
And gambolled on earth

And only the poet
With wings to his brain
Can mount him and ride him
Without any rein,
The stallion of heaven,
The steed of the skies,
The horse of the singer
Who sings as he flies.

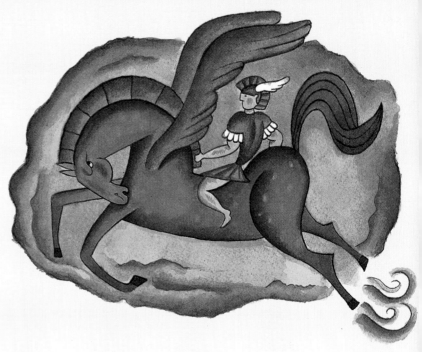

Sphinx
by Deborah Chandra

As the sun
Is going down,
And shadows mix
With yellow sand,
He rises slowly,
Stretches, stands,
Wades into the Nile to wash
Mummy-dust and sand fleas off—
Licks heavy paws
With heavy tongue
Until the cool night air is gone.
While on Egyptian earth
He drops dry purrs,
Ground out like powdered rock.

NOTHING AT ALL

by *Julia Pferdehirt*
Illustrated by *Marie LaFrance*

The Eastern Kingdom stretched ten days' ride along the seacoast. Traders followed dusty roads from village to village, leaving kitchen knives or plow blades and taking away a winter's lacework, bags of spun wool, or great kegs of cider. The laws were few and fair, and the land was good. From harvest to harvest, all those who lived between the western mountains and the sea paid their taxes, held holiday each year on the king's name day, and generally kept the peace.

In a small village near the foothills, there lived a remarkable family. The oldest child could run with such speed that people called him Seena, which means "The Antelope Runs." The second child was a story weaver who told tales of great wit and beauty. Everyone called her Ista, "The Sun Laughs."

When the third, and last, child was born, the villagers waited to see what her gift might be. Some thought she would become a great healer; others suggested a famous sculptor or a wise counsellor to the king.

Years passed as this girl-child grew. She was gentle, kind, fun-loving, and clever. She made friends easily and would have been a joy to any parent's heart—except that she did nothing extraordinary. Her hands had no special skill, and her mind was no keener nor her judgement clearer than other people's. When her parents saw nothing unique in their daughter, they were shocked, and as time passed, the people in the village began calling her Ona, which means "Nothing at All."

One autumn the villagers heard rumbling in the western mountains. Sometimes the rumbling became a great roar that echoed across the valley. The oldest woman in the village said then that a dragon was on the rampage, but no one believed her, of course.

Nor did anyone believe her when the forest on the western mountains burned red for most of a week. Only when the streams from the western hills flowed with steaming water, and the mountain villagers fled with their bundles and their fear, did the people finally believe.

The villagers asked Ona's brother, Seena, to run to the king for help. Ona's sister, Ista, composed the message, pleading for the ruler to take the villagers under his protection. Scarcely had Seena disappeared on the eastern road than the people began gathering their possessions together. The roaring in the west told them that they, too, would soon be refugees, fleeing the dragon.

As the villagers prepared to leave, Ona wandered through the streets asking the old people what they knew about dragons. They knew very little. The oldest woman told her that dragons loved few things in the world besides gold, cruelty, and riddling.

"My mother once told me that dragons are magical creatures," the old woman said, "and that they riddle because they are cruel. But if you defeat them, they must give you whatever you ask for. My mother didn't say why, and I don't even know if it's true."

A neighbor told a similar tale about a dragon that lost its magic because it could not guess a riddle. Other than that, the villagers knew nothing. They were terrified.

That night Ona cried out as dragon shapes filled her sleep. She woke shaking and rose to look out the window at the western mountains. If the dragon pursues me even in my dreams, she thought, how will running away do any good? We have children and grandparents to slow us, and nothing at all to hold the dragon back.

With those words, "nothing at all," Ona nearly stopped breathing. She gripped the edge of the window sill and stared like a sleepwalker into the darkness outside.

"Hold it back," she whispered to herself. "Nothing at all to hold it back." It was almost dawn when the foolish, impossible idea came to her.

Before sunrise, the people began their sad journey to the east, their rattling carts and bleating sheep raising clouds of dust. Ona took her basket and blanket and walked west toward the meadow. In the panic, she was not missed.

Ona spread her blanket on the ground in the very centre of the meadow and sat facing the mountains. Throughout the afternoon she sat, small and unmoving. Toward evening, she unwrapped some of the soft round buns her mother had made for the eastern journey. Tears dropped onto the napkin as she ate.

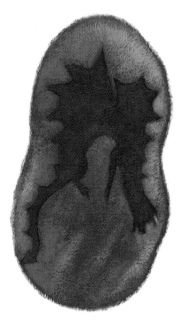

When the sun reached the crest of the western mountains, Ona saw the dragon dark against it. She saw its great wingspan and its long, reaching neck. The beast began its flight toward the meadow, and as it approached, Ona could see its claws and the black smoke curling from its nostrils.

The dragon landed with surprising grace in front of her, but Ona did not move. When the dragon spoke, its voice was low, hoarse, and rumbling.

"You are a small one to be so foolish. Why did you not flee like the others?"

Its eyes narrowed, and cruel smoke rose slowly from its snout. Ona watched as its tail swept the ground only inches from her blanket.

"Speak!" said the dragon. "Amuse me, or I shall destroy you."

Now Ona spoke the words she had so carefully planned. "I have heard," she said slowly, "that you are a great riddler, and I could not imagine such a thing. I have come to see if it is true." She forced herself to look directly into the dragon's fierce eyes.

Perhaps the beast was amused. It stood silent for so long that Ona began to feel the coldness of the ground through the blanket. She heard the dragon's breath, low and grating. It was a terrible sound, a sound of waiting and trapping and great claws toying with helpless prey. She held her body still by sheer force of will.

It was almost a relief when the dragon finally spoke. "You?" it roared. "You? Fool, give me one reason why I should not flame you to ashes!"

Again Ona's dark eyes lifted to the dragon's great burning ones and held them. She heard herself say, "Because then you will never know the riddle. And I shall never know if you can answer it."

The dragon's tail swept great arcs across the ground, scraping the meadow raw, clear through the dark topsoil to the rock below. The grating sound of its breathing became a rumble as dark smoke poured from its nostrils. Suddenly, terribly, the beast bellowed and leaped into the air, all wings and hot breath. Ona closed her eyes, telling herself she would only be the first to die.

"Very well," shouted the dragon. "Tell me this riddle of

yours, and we shall see. But hurry, I do not waste my time with fools."

Now, for the first time, Ona moved. She stood up and faced the dragon. Behind the great creature, she could see smoke from mountain villages, charred to smoldering sticks by the dragon's flame. She had no real hope that her own home and crops would be spared, but she was determined to gain precious minutes for those who were running to safety.

"Listen carefully, dragon," she said loudly. "I will only say the riddle once. No true riddler needs to hear it a second time."

The dark smoke from the dragon's nostrils gave way to flame that singed the blanket. The girl smelled burned wool, but refused to lower her eyes. I play this game for all or nothing, she thought.

Speaking in a firm voice, she said, "Here is the riddle. . . ."

"Nothing can defeat you,
    yet it may,
to gain the moment,
    to bar the way,
in silence and stone,
    in dark and in day.
One clue I will give you,
    no more will I say;
you must seek and find nothing
    to win this play."

The girl turned her back to the beast, drew the blanket around her head and shoulders, and sat down.

For nearly an hour, the two shapes huddled in silence. Then the dragon began to mutter to itself and shuffle back and forth like a prisoner pacing a cell. Ona ate some bread and drank from a water bottle. Although she did not turn her head, she could hear the dragon's words becoming louder and louder behind her.

"What game is this?" it rumbled. "Nothing can defeat me! Nothing! Do you hear, human?" Looking at the girl's turned back only magnified the dragon's growing rage. It stomped, raising billows of dust and raking its great tail over the stony ground.

Near sunset Ona could hear the dragon repeating bits of her riddle. For an hour it whispered the words "to gain the moment" over and over. She felt the creature's hot breath on her back as the sun slipped below the mountains and the grey skies dwindled to blackness. Then she sat, wrapped in her blanket, waiting for the sunrise. She hoped to be alive to see it.

During the coldest hour of the night, a howl slapped the girl from her half-sleep. The dragon was roaring and shrieking, lashing its tail and crying out in frustration and rage. "Tell me, human," it screamed, "how am I to seek nothing? If this is a lie, I will show you no mercy!" This last the beast whispered with half-closed eyes, the smoke from its nostrils seeping out and sinking to the ground like a horrid creeping thing.

Ona thought she might scream from pure terror. She gripped the blanket about her with both hands and closed her eyes so she could not see the flames as the dragon flew in circles above her. Even when the heat beat against her face and the fire singed her hair, she did not move. Only as dawn approached and the dragon flew toward the shadow of the mountains did Ona open her eyes to watch its fiery trail.

The beast did not return.

Sunrise was cold. Ona huddled on the hard earth and trembled. A clinging fog crept up from the foothills, turning the valley into a bowl of rolling grey smoke. Straining her eyes, Ona searched from north to south and back again, waiting for the shadow that would mark the dragon's return. She was terrified the beast might come without her seeing. Although she had no weapon, she did not want to be caught unaware. She pushed away the thought that she might scream and run mad with fear into the hills.

When the dragon did come, Ona was surprised by the silence of its flight. The creature circled three, then four times over the small, still figure on the ground. At last, folding its wings like great fans, the dragon settled in the open meadow in front of her.

"Human," the beast whispered, its voice scraping

in Ona's ears like claws. Ona raised her eyes. The dragon continued to speak, low and harsh. "Did you know about the magic when you came?"

Ona was not about to give any answer that would allow the dragon to trick her, so she simply nodded.

"Then you expected to die, human," growled the dragon. "You knew that if I answered your riddle, you would lose and I would flame you to ashes." Tendrils of dark smoke crawled from its nostrils as the dragon began the slow pacing back and forth that Ona had seen during the night.

The dragon paced; Ona trembled. Neither of them spoke.

The silence continued. Ona had stopped wondering if she would die when the dragon hissed, "Tell me the answer, human. Or do you have no magic to lose?"

"What do you mean?" Ona asked, her voice cracking. Her mind was working frantically to figure out what the creature was saying. Suddenly, she recalled the neighbor's tale about the dragon that lost its magic. If only she knew more!

"Do not play with me!" screamed the beast. "You spoke the riddle, and I have not answered it. Yet I do not hear you give the cry of victory and I do not hear the answer to this riddle from your own mouth. You have defeated me and yet you say nothing! What do you want?"

At that moment, she knew the old people's confused snatches of memory had been true. The dragon did not know the answer. She had riddled and won, against all hope or possibility! And now . . . yes, what now? Evidently, the dragon expected her to say or do something.

Ona rose, dropping the blanket behind her. When she spoke, her voice was firm. "Dragon," she said, "I did speak the riddle to you and I have not heard your answer. I am nothing, yet I have defeated you." Ona's voice grew louder as she spoke:

> "Nothing can defeat you,
>   yet it may,
>   to gain the moment,
>   to bar the way,
>   in silence and stone,
>   in dark and in day.
>   One clue I will give you,
>   no more will I say;
>   you must seek and find nothing
>   to win this play."

Ona waited, watching the dragon closely. In a moment its eyes flashed and its brow raised, as if in surprise.

"That is correct, dragon," Ona said. "It is I who am Nothing, and it is I who have defeated you. I kept you here to gain time for my people as they ran from your evil greed. I barred the way in silence and stone. Consider, dragon, whether you saw me move or heard my voice in day or night. You did not!"

Now the joy of unexpected, even impossible, victory filled her. Ona cried up at the dragon, "I am Ona! Ona means Nothing at All! I am Nothing, and you did not find me!"

Now the dragon spoke so low, Ona could scarcely hear. "I see it is so. I have been defeated. What do you want? If I do not grant your wish, the magic of my flame will die."

"Go," commanded Ona. "Fly to the caves on the peak of the ancient mountains where no humans will ever build huts or plant gardens. If you ever return, dragon, or if one human dies under your flame, your magic will die. Go and never come back!"

The dragon raised its head and howled its fury and impotence and despair. Then the beast bowed its great, scaly head and said, "You have spoken, human. I will go. Still, your people are fools to call you Ona. Among my kind you would be called Kima, Kima Reetana."

The dragon spread its wings and flamed out of sight over the western mountains, leaving Ona to gather her things and return to the village.

Some days later Seena returned to the village as well. When the people had not seen smoke from their burning homes, they had sent their swiftest runner to investigate. He could hardly believe what he found.

Seena raced back to his family and friends on the muddy banks of the river to the east. He ran without stopping, swift as the antelope, to bring the news. "Ona was waiting for me," he panted. "The dragon has gone." The word "gone" formed in each mind and was whispered, passed like a precious stone from hand to hand. "Ona riddled with the dragon and won!" Seena continued. "She made the dragon leave."

The people collected their belongings and children and headed home. Along the road Ista, the story weaver, repeated the tale of Ona's riddle and the dragon's defeat. Each person passed the story on to the next, telling how Ona had sat in the meadow without moving or speaking to win time for the villager's escape. The people could not walk quickly enough to satisfy their desire to see Ona, and to see the impossible miracle of their homes and crops still standing.

The celebration when the villagers returned was like the name days of ten kings! Ista was asked to tell the tale over and over, until the moon rose full and the grandmothers nodded over the sleeping children in their laps. Men and women alike held Ona's hands in theirs and wept. They were alive, and she had done a thing beyond the most amazing story!

From that time, the village celebrated Ona's victory each year. The holiday was called Bar-reet, meaning "The Great Riddle." Each year Ista, the story weaver, told the tale of Ona and the dragon to the assembled villagers, and each year the king sent a gift in Ona's honor. And always her name was spoken with joy and respect. Only she was no longer called Ona. Now all the kingdom knew her as Kima Reetana—"Brave One, Who Riddles with Dragons."

ABOUT THE AUTHOR   JULIA PFERDEHIRT

Julia Pferdehirt's favorite activity is writing stories for children. She says that if she were stranded on a desert island she would want a lot of books—science fiction, true adventures, and fairytales— especially dragon stories. Julia is married and the mother of three teenage daughters. *Nothing at All* was first told long ago to her daughters as a bedtime story. Now Julia travels around her home state of Wisconsin dressed as an 1850s station mistress on the Underground Railroad. She tells stories of the fight to help runaway slaves reach freedom in Canada.

The Lore of the Unicorn

by Bruce Coville
Illustrated by France Brassard

What is a unicorn?
At first glance, the answer may seem so obvious that the question itself is silly. Everyone knows that a unicorn is a horse with a horn stuck in the middle of its forehead.

Right?

Well, yes—and no. The answer is much more complicated, and considerably more interesting, than that.

What unicorns actually do look like has been a matter of some dispute for several centuries now. Some old accounts give them white bodies and red heads, with a short, three-colored horn. Others give them elephant's feet, a boar's tail, and other equally improbable traits.

Oddly, while writers continued to disagree over what unicorns look like, artists kept coming back to the same basic idea: an animal much like a horse, but (in the better pictures) lighter and more graceful, with many goat-like qualities.

In particular, you should expect a unicorn to have a silky beard and hoofs that are split, or cloven, like those of a goat.

But even though we can describe a unicorn as having some of the traits of both these animals, in truth these creatures are far more magical than either a goat or horse could ever hope to be. Even the best descriptions fall far short of what you would see if you actually met a unicorn some moonlit night beneath an apple tree. (Not a bad place to look, by the way. Some unicorns are wisdom personified, and wisdom can, indeed, often be found beneath an apple tree on such a night.)

Unicorns have many strange abilities. But of all the things they can do, it seems we are most fascinated by their power to heal. For the touch of a unicorn's horn can pull us away from death, toward immortality.

Unfortunately for the unicorn, the horn

retains its power even without a unicorn attached—which has led people to hunt it rather ferociously.

The basic method for catching a unicorn is fairly simple. A pure young woman is taken into the woods and placed beneath a tree. Since unicorns are irresistibly attracted to such young ladies, if there is a unicorn in the vicinity, it will come and lay its head in this maiden's lap. At this point, she may sing to it, or slip a golden bridle over its head.

Once the unicorn has been tamed in this manner, the hunters leap out from hiding and either capture or slaughter the beast. When they do, the greatest prize, of course, is the horn itself. (Though some people also believe there is a precious jewel, a "carbuncle," hidden underneath the horn.)

The correct term for the horn is "alicorn," a word some people think was invented simply because "unicorn horn" sounds so awkward.

Alicorns are among the most powerful of magical items. They were prized by popes and kings because they provided protection against all manner of evil, including epilepsy, pestilence, and poisoning. A horn set in the middle of a table would begin to sweat, or form a dew, if any of the foodstuffs had been poisoned. Even a little powder filed from such a horn was an antidote to the most toxic substances. Small wonder that in a place like fourteenth-century Italy, where poisoning was a common way to deal with one's enemies, these horns were considered treasures indeed.

As might be expected, an item both so valuable (horns sometimes sold for ten times their weight in gold) and so rare (some legends have it that there is never more than one unicorn on Earth at a time) was a great temptation for frauds.

With so many people selling false alicorns, it was necessary to find a way to determine which were real. Some of the tests included:

- Drawing a ring on the floor with the alicorn. A spider placed in such a ring would not be able to cross the line, and in fact, would starve to death trapped within the circle.
- Placing the horn in water, which would cause the water to bubble and seem as if it were boiling, even though it remained cold.
- Placing a piece of silk upon a burning coal, and then laying the horn on top of the silk. If the horn was truly an alicorn, the silk would not be burned.
- Bringing the horn near a poisonous plant or animal, which would burst and die in reaction to it.

The trade in alicorns was very real in the Middle Ages, and many noble houses listed one of the mystical horns among its treasures.

However most of us today would agree it is far better to leave a unicorn's horn where it belongs: on top of its head!

With its horn properly in place, a unicorn can do many wonderful things. One of the most well known is purifying water for other animals, a trick known as "water conning." Generally, this takes place where there is some venomous animal haunting the water hole. The serpent, or whatever, will slip out at night and poison the water. But at dawn the unicorn comes and dips its horn in the pool. Immediately, the water is clean and pure once more.

Three famous warriors have been connected with unicorns—Julius Caesar, Alexander the Great, and Genghis Khan. Caesar's connection was minor; he wrote of a unicorn that lived in the Hercynian Forest. But of Alexander it is actually said that he rode a unicorn—the famous Bucephalus, who many think was only a horse, but others claim was a unicorn.

France Brossard

(Considering the fame Bucephalus gained as a warhorse, he was probably a relative of the kar-ka-dann, which you will meet below.) It is also said that Alexander and his men once had a battle with a tribe of unicorns. As for Genghis Khan, it is written that in the year 1206, he set out with a great army to conquer India. As he was standing in a mountain pass overlooking that great country, a one-horned beast came running up to him and knelt three times in token of reverence. The Mighty Khan took this as a signal from his dead father, and turned his army back.

Clearly, unicorns are known the world over. In addition to the horned horse-like/goat-like creature we are familiar with, there is the Chinese unicorn, called the K'i-lin, which had a multi-colored body and (some said) a horn four metres long.

K'i-lin was very special to the Chinese. It was a creature of great power and wisdom, and its appearance was always a sign of good fortune. The most famous example happened over 2500 years ago, when the K'i-lin came to a young woman named Yen Chen-tsai. Into her hand it dropped a tablet made of jade, the beautiful green stone used in much Chinese art. On the stone was a message, prophesying that she would become the mother of a "throneless king."

The prophecy was true, for Yen Chen-tsai became the mother of the great Chinese sage, Confucius. Confucius never wore a crown or commanded men. Yet his teachings did as much to shape China as the power of many kings and warlords combined.

It was said that K'i-lin walked so softly its hoofs made no sound. Some believed that this was because it was so soft-hearted it did not want to crush the blades of grass beneath its feet. It had a voice like a thousand wind chimes, avoided fighting at all costs, and lived for a thousand years.

How different was the unicorn of Persia, the fierce and ferocious kar-ka-dann, a terrible beast that could attack and kill even an elephant! The only thing that could tame this savage animal was the ringdove; so soothing did the kar-ka-dann find their gentle calls, that it would lie peacefully beneath a tree where they were

Franca Brassard

singing, for hours on end. Though other animals couldn't even graze in the kar-ka-dann's territory, the ringdove was actually allowed to perch on the beast's horn.

Despite its worldwide fame, there are those who believe there are no more unicorns. One reason people give for their disappearance is that when Noah built the Ark, the unicorns didn't make it on board, either because they were too large, or too silly—playing games and frisking about until Noah couldn't wait any longer.

Others think they were simply hunted into extinction.

Still others believe that the unicorns left when the world became less sympathetic to the old magic, fleeing to someplace better suited to their strange beauty.

Saddest of all are those who believe there never were any unicorns to begin with.

Where did they come from, where have they gone, were they ever here at all?

The truth is, no one knows for certain.

But here's what I believe: wherever else they may have come from, unicorns live inside the true believer's heart, which means that as long as we can dream, there will be unicorns.

ABOUT THE AUTHOR   BRUCE COVILLE

Bruce Coville was born in Syracuse, New York where he now lives with his wife, youngest child, three cats, and a dog. Before he was able to make a living as a writer Bruce was a gravedigger, a toymaker, a magazine editor, and a door-to-door salesperson. He has written nearly fifty books for young readers as well as poems, plays, short stories, and newspaper articles. Bruce has won or been nominated for nearly forty book awards.

Mythical Creatures

All over the world there are mythical creatures. I am going to talk about three of these mythical creatures—dragons, unicorns, and griffins.

Dragons come in different shapes and have strange abilities. Some have huge wings, but others have not. Many have four legs and others are like serpents. Some are born with many heads; some are able to grow two or more heads if something happens to their first head. Most of them can breathe fire and can speak different languages.

Unicorns are usually found in Europe and Asia. They look like horses with a twisted horn on their forehead. Their horns have miraculous power to clean dirty water when it comes in contact with the water. Also, unicorns have the rear legs of an antelope, which enables them to run swiftly.

Griffins are ferocious creatures found mostly in Europe. They are a strange mixture with the head of an eagle, the body of a lion, the tail of a snake, and two large wings. Griffins are enemies of horses.

These are only three of the many mythical creatures. There are many more, but don't expect to see any because they are now extinct.

by Joey Mo
Age 10

Legendary Animals

Long ago, there were legendary animals. Some of them were dragons and unicorns. They were mighty and fierce. They scared people and destroyed great kingdoms. Many people were afraid of these legendary animals.

Dragons were the most feared by people because sometimes they would gobble people up. Here are some of the most feared and famous dragons: Tiamat-first dragon in the world, Shen Lung-controlled the weather, Hydra-five-headed dragon (if you cut off one head, two more will grow back), Basilisk-gave off a poisonous gas, which had no cure and looks could kill.

Unicorns were gentle animals. They were like horses except that they had a horn in the middle of their forehead. Most people don't believe in unicorns. A unicorn had a horse's body, a goat's head, and horse's hooves. The horn on it's forehead proved that it was the leader of animals. Once a unicorn put its horn into the water and the water became clear and fresh to drink. Unicorns were magical creatures.

Dragons and unicorns are only some of all the legendary animals. There are many, many more.

by Mary Wong
Grade 6

I like writing because I like to read my work and I can also learn from what I write.

45

Wings to the Sun

by Richard Scrimger
Illustrated by Josée Masse

Daedalus and Icarus

Long ago in ancient Greece, there lived a great inventor named Daedalus. Because of his fame, King Minos of Crete ordered Daedalus to build a mighty maze for him, called the Labyrinth. It was so intricate, so full of twists and dead ends and unexpected turnings, that no one who ventured in could get out. Minos used the Labyrinth as a kind of jail for the Minotaur, a beast who was terrorizing the countryside.

King Minos was so pleased with the Labyrinth that he decided to keep Daedalus in Crete forever, to create more wonderful inventions for him. So Daedalus and his young son, Icarus, were imprisoned in a high tower.

At once, wily Daedalus set to work to discover a way to escape. As he paced back and forth, he watched great cranes and eagles circling high above the tower. If only he and his son could fly, how easy it would be to escape from Minos! As his father watched the circling birds, Icarus collected the feathers that sometimes floated down.

Daedalus thought long and deeply about how birds flew, making notes on wax tablets with a stylus. Meanwhile, Icarus collected more and more feathers. Soon, the master inventor was ready. He used melted wax from the tablets to fasten feathers to strips of cloth which he tied to their arms and bodies. Then he and Icarus stood on top of the tower with their arms spread, the wind rippling their new wings. "Remember," Daedalus warned his son, "don't try to fly too high, or the heat from the sun will melt the wax from your wings!" Icarus nodded, and the two of them leapt into space.

It was a wonderful flight. They soared and glided and swooped away from Crete. Below lay the blue, blue sea, and the sky was all around them. Daedalus flew steadily toward the mainland, but Icarus, full of the wild joy of his flight, circled higher and higher. The higher he flew, the hotter the sun shone on him, and the softer grew the wax of his wings. Suddenly, the wax burst into flame, the feathers fell away, and Icarus was no longer flying, but falling. Daedalus cried out in horror as his son hurtled past him and crashed into the waves.

Heartbroken, Daedalus landed on the nearest island, ripped off his own wings and vowed never to fly again. In honor of his son, he called the place he landed Icaria.

Icarus Sunset

Wheeling across the sky at dusk, wings outspread
Long-feathered fingers cherishing the wind,
The eagle came to them.
They watched her, high on the tower, a man and a boy
Watched the soaring minister of the air.
See, said the man, See, Icarus, how
She turns into the wind to rise,
Away to fall
Mark how she steers herself.
And the man thought, It is freedom, escape from prison
And the boy thought, It is power.
Remember, Icarus, with the wings on your back, to
Follow me, do as I do.
Yes, father.
But the boy was watching the eagle still
As she flew into the heart of the setting sun
And vanished into gold.

Long labored Daedalus, making his freedom
Carefully choosing the feathers, cunningly
Shaping the wax,
And each day the boy and he waited for the eagle
As the dusk gathered round them
And the sun fell into darkness.

Now, father? said the boy, poised on
The parapet, feathered arms wide, facing the morning.
Now, said the maker, leaping.

The wind bore them gently away,
On its back they rode as birds do
As eagles, as gods.
Follow, Icarus, cried his father
Remember, follow me.
But the boy, deaf with power, heard only
The Sun's voice, coaxing him higher.
Rise with me, Icarus, whispered the god,
I will welcome you.

Far below, Daedalus, fearful with knowledge
Strained his eyes upward, waiting for the
Hurtling blackened body that
Passed without speaking and vanished
Into the sea.

Savitri and Satyavan

by Madhur Jaffrey
Illustrated by Taddeus Majewski

Once upon a time, there lived a king and queen who, after many years of being childless, gave birth to a daughter.

She was the most beautiful baby her parents could have hoped for, and they named her Savitri.

When Savitri grew up and it was time for her to marry, her father said to her, "Dearest child, we hate to part with you. You have given us the greatest joy that humans can ever know. But it is time for you to start a family of your own. Is there any man you wish to marry?"

"No, father," replied Savitri, "I have not yet met a man I would care to spend my life with."

"Perhaps we should send for pictures of all the nobles in the country. You might come upon a face you like," said the king and he sent his court painter to bring back portraits of all the nobles and rulers in the country.

Savitri examined the portraits, one after the other, and shook her head. The men in the portraits all looked so very ordinary, even though they were emperors, kings, and princes.

The king then said to his daughter, "It might be best if you went to all the big cities of the world to find a husband for yourself. I will provide you with the proper escort of people, elephants, camels, and horses. Good luck. I hope you can find a man to love."

Savitri set out with a large procession of people, elephants, camels, and horses. In her effort to visit all the cities of the world, she had to cross many oceans and deserts. She did this fearlessly. But she never found a man she could love.

When she returned home, her father said to her, "You have looked in all the big cities of the world and have found no man that you wish to marry. Perhaps you should now search through all the forests of the world."

Savitri set out again with a large procession of people, elephants, camels, and horses, and began searching through all the forests of the world. She did this fearlessly.

She had looked through the last forest and was just about to return home when she came upon a young man who was cutting wood.

"What is your name?" she asked.

"Satyavan, Your Highness," he replied.

"Please do not address me as 'Your Highness'," she said, "my name is Savitri. What do you do for a living?"

"I do nothing much," the young man replied. "I have very old, blind parents. I live with them in a small, thatched cottage at the edge of the forest. Every morning I go out to cut wood and gather food. In the evening I make a fire for my parents, cook their dinner, and feed them. That is all I do."

Savitri returned to her father's palace and said, "Dearest mother and father. I have finally found a man to love and marry. His name is Satyavan and he lives in a cottage by a forest not too far from here."

"But will you be able to live a simple life in a simple cottage?" asked her father. "This young man obviously has no money."

"That makes no difference at all to me," Savitri said. "He is capable, honest, good, and caring. That is what I respect and love him for."

The king sent a message to the blind couple's cottage saying that Princess Savitri wished to marry their son, Satyavan. When Satyavan arrived home that evening with his heavy load of wood, his parents said, "There are messengers here from the king. Princess Savitri wishes to marry you."

"I love the young lady in question," replied Satyavan, "but it will be impossible to marry her. She has money, jewels, elephants, camels, and servants. What can *I* offer her?"

Tears rolled down the faces of his blind parents. "Son," cried the mother, "we never told you this, but before you were born, your father too was a ruler with a kingdom of his own. His wicked brother blinded us and stole our birthright. You should have been born a prince and heir to the kingdom, quite worthy of the beautiful Savitri. We have fallen on hard times, but if you two love each other, why should you not marry? Who knows what the future has in store for anybody?"

So a message was sent back to the king saying that Satyavan had agreed to the match.

On the day of the wedding, the king and queen held a huge reception. Everyone of any importance was invited.

That is how it happened that the wisest sage in the kingdom appeared at the scene.

Just before the wedding ceremony, the sage took the king aside and whispered, "It is my duty to warn you. The young man your daughter is to marry is decent and of good character, but his stars are crossed. He will die very shortly. This marriage would be a tragic mistake."

The king felt ill when he heard this. He called his daughter and told her what the sage had said, adding, "Perhaps it is best to call the marriage off."

"No, father," Savitri said solemnly, "I will marry Satyavan, whatever our future may hold."

Savitri was no fool, however. She had heard that the sage knew of heavenly remedies for earthly problems.

"Oh dearest sage," Savitri said to him, "surely there is a way I can prevent my husband from dying. You, in your great wisdom, must offer me some hope. There must be something I can do?"

The sage thought deeply. "You can extend your husband's life by fasting. Eat nothing but fruit, roots, and leaves for a year, and Satyavan will live for those twelve months. After that he must die."

With a sense of doom hanging over the bride's family, the wedding did take place. The groom and his parents were told nothing of what the future held for them.

Savitri began to lead a simple life with her husband and parents-in-law. Early each morning, Satyavan set out for the forest to cut wood and to forage for food. When he was gone, Savitri made the beds, swept the house, and shepherded her in-laws around wherever they wished to go. She also prayed and fasted.

One day Savitri's mother-in-law said to her, "Child, we know how rich a family you come from. Since we have lost our kingdom, we can offer you no fineries, but Satyavan does collect enough food for all of us. We have noticed that you eat just fruit, roots, and leaves and never touch any grain. That is not a healthy diet. We are beginning to worry about you."

"Oh, please do not worry about me," begged Savitri. "I love to eat fruit."

The twelve months were almost over. On the very last day, Savitri got up with her husband and announced that she would accompany him into the forest.

"Child, what will you do in the forest? The work is hard and there are all kinds of dangerous animals," said her mother-in-law.

"Do stay home," said Satyavan, "the forest is not a comfortable place."

"I have travelled through all the forests of the world. I was not uncomfortable and I was not frightened. Let me go with you today."

Satyavan had no answer for his wife. He loved her a lot and trusted her instincts. "Come along then, we'd better start quickly. The sun is almost up."

So they set out towards the heart of the forest.

Once there, Satyavan climbed a tree and began to saw off its dried-up branches.

It was a scorchingly hot day in May. The trees had shed the last withered yellowing leaves. Savitri looked for a cool spot to sit down and just could not find any. Her heart was beating like a two-sided drum. Any moment now the year would end.

"Ahhh…" came a cry from Satyavan.

Savitri ran towards him. "Are you all right?"

"I have a piercing headache."

"Come down from the tree. It's the heat. I will run and find some shade." Savitri found a banyan tree and helped Satyavan towards it. Many of the banyan tree's branches had gone deep into the earth and come up again to form a deliciously cool grove. The leaves rustled gently to fan the couple.

"Put your head in my lap," Savitri said to Satyavan, "and rest."

Satyavan put his head down, gave a low moan, and died.

Savitri looked up. There, in the distance coming towards her, was Yamraj, the King of the Underworld. He was riding a male water buffalo, and Savitri knew he was coming to claim Satyavan's soul. She turned to the banyan tree and implored, "Banyan tree, banyan tree, look after my husband. Shield him and keep him cool. I will return one day to claim him."

Yamraj took Satyavan's soul and started to ride away. Savitri followed on foot. She followed for miles and miles. Yamraj finally turned around and said, "Why are you following me, woman?"

"You are taking my husband's soul away. Why don't you take me as well? I cannot live without him."

"Go back, go back to your home and do not bother me," Yamraj said.

But Savitri kept following.

Yamraj turned around again. "Stop following me, woman," he cried.

Savitri paid no heed to him.

"Well, woman," said Yamraj, "I can see that you are quite determined. I will grant you just one wish. As long as you do not ask for your husband's soul."

"May my in-laws have their sight back?" asked Savitri.

"All right, all right," said Yamraj, "now go home."

After several more miles Yamraj glanced back. There was Savitri, still following.

"You really are quite persistent," Yamraj said. "I'll grant you one other wish. Just remember, do not ask for your husband's soul."

"Could my father-in-law get back the kingdom he lost?" Savitri asked.

"Yes, yes," said Yamraj, "now go, go."

Several miles later, Yamraj looked back again.

Savitri was still following.

"I do not understand you. I've granted two wishes and yet you keep following me. This is the last wish I am offering you. Remember, you can ask for anything but your husband's soul."

"May I be the mother of many sons?" Savitri asked.

"Yes, yes," Yamraj said. "Now go. Go back home."

Several miles later Yamraj looked back only to see Savitri still there. "Why are you still following me?" Yamraj asked. "I have already granted your wish of many sons."

"How will I have many sons?" Savitri asked. "You are carrying away the soul of the only husband I have. I will never marry again. You have granted me a false wish. It can never come true."

"I have had enough," Yamraj said. "I am quite exhausted. Here, take back your husband's soul."

Savitri rushed back to the banyan tree so her husband's body and soul could be joined again.

"O banyan tree," she said, "thank you for looking after my husband. In the years to come, may all married women come to you and offer thanks and prayers."

Satyavan opened his eyes and said, "My headache has gone."

"Yes," said Savitri, "thanks to the kind banyan tree that offered us its shade. Let us go home now where a surprise awaits you. I will not tell you what it is."

Satyavan put his arm around his wife's shoulders and they began to walk slowly back home.

ABOUT THE AUTHOR MADHUR JAFFREY

Madhur Jaffrey has lived most of her adult life in London and New York, but she grew up in Delhi, India. This background along with her talent for cooking and writing has led her to become a well-known author of cookbooks on Indian cuisine. Madhur is also a stage and screen actress, journalist, and illustrator. She has won several awards for her illustrations.

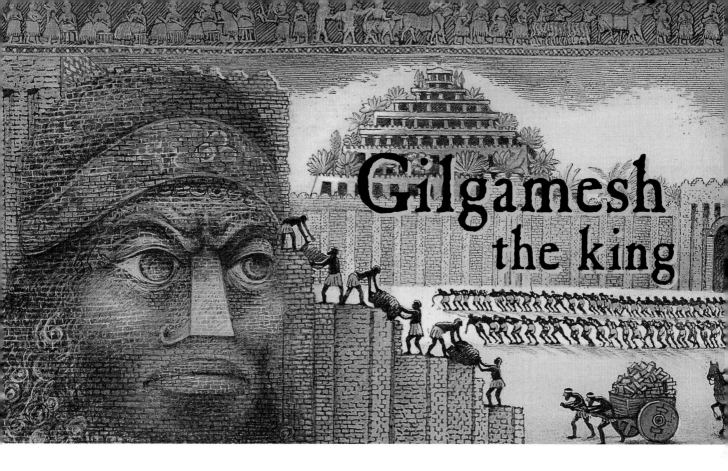

Gilgamesh the king

Retold and Illustrated by Ludmila Zeman

Long ago in the land of Mesopotamia, a king by the name of Gilgamesh was sent by the Sun God to rule over the city of Uruk.

Gilgamesh was part god and part man. He looked human, but he did not know what it was to be human. He had power and wealth, but he was not happy. He had everything except friends. He was always alone. Because of this he grew bitter and cruel.

One day, he decided to show how strong and powerful he was and make the people remember him forever.

So it was that Gilgamesh ordered a great wall to be built around the city. He ordered the men to leave their jobs and families to work on it. He made the women bring food. Children were kept away so no one would stop to play with them. At first, the people helped willingly. Their king must have good reason for wanting the wall. Was an enemy planning to attack the city?

But as the wall got higher and higher, the people grew restless. How high did it have to be? It went up higher than any wall in the world, but Gilgamesh pushed on day and night. Men fainted from work and hunger. Food grew scarce. The people cried out for mercy, begging Gilgamesh to stop, but he would not listen. In despair, they prayed to the Sun God for help.

The Sun God heard their prayers and ordered the creation of another man as strong as Gilgamesh. His name was Enkidu. He was made from the clay of the earth.

Since Gilgamesh had learned nothing from living with people, Enkidu was sent to live with the animals of the forest. As he got to know the animals, he learned to care for them. But he did not know human kindness for he had never seen another person.

The first man Enkidu saw he did not like. It was a hunter chasing animals through the forest, trying to kill them. Why would anyone want to do that? Enkidu wondered. He rushed to help his friends. He threw the hunter from his chariot and rescued the wounded animals. The hunter ran back to Uruk to warn Gilgamesh about the new danger in the forest. He called Enkidu "the strongest man in the world."

Gilgamesh was furious. "There is no one as strong as I am," he said. "Bring this creature to me so I can prove it. I will destroy him in front of all the people of Uruk." The hunter said that he could not capture so strong a wild man by himself. "Then," said Gilgamesh, "we will trick him into coming. Take the singer Shamhat. Let her lure him here with her songs and charms."

It was said that the only person in Uruk who did not love Shamhat was Gilgamesh and that was because he loved no one. She was the most beautiful woman in the city and the finest singer in the temple. But could she tame the wild man?

The hunter did not want to return to the forest to be made a fool of again, but he dared not argue with Gilgamesh, or disobey him.

The hunter led Shamhat to the place in the forest where he had last seen Enkidu. He left her alone and fled back to the city.

As night fell, Shamhat played her harp and sang in the darkness. Her voice cast a spell over the forest. Enkidu walked toward the sound then stopped behind a tree. He had never seen anything so lovely. He approached her slowly so as not to frighten her.

Shamhat saw Enkidu and stopped singing. He looked more like a beast than a man, but she knew he would not harm her. No one had ever looked at her with so much tenderness. In the days that followed, Shamhat taught him to speak and to sing and she fell in love with him. Enkidu promised he would stay with her always.

Shamhat was frightened. Enkidu must not go near the city of Uruk where Gilgamesh was waiting to destroy him. But Enkidu refused to listen. He was not afraid. He would fight to the death for her.

The saddest moment for Enkidu was leaving his animal friends. They gathered to watch him go. They could not understand why he was abandoning them and he could not explain.

Each day from morning until dusk Gilgamesh watched from his tower on top of the great wall of Uruk waiting for Shamhat to return. Everyone in the city had heard of the wild man who might come from the forest and save them from their cruel king. Gilgamesh knew what they were thinking. He would kill the stranger in front of all the people of Uruk so no one would think of challenging his rule.

Shamhat was worried. Could Enkidu defeat Gilgamesh? What would people think of this wild creature? To make him look more like other men, she cut his hair and tore part of her robe to cover him. But Enkidu kept his horned crown in memory of his animal friends. Shamhat pointed to Uruk in the distance. Enkidu was dazzled. He had not imagined how beautiful a city could be.

The next morning the people gathered to watch as Shamhat and Enkidu approached the gate. Gilgamesh had ordered work on the wall stopped for the day so all could see his victory. He stood on top of the wall and shouted at Enkidu, "I am master of this city and its people! No one enters without my permission! I dare you to come up here and fight me!" Enkidu climbed the wall. "I am ready!" he shouted back.

It was the most frightening battle the people of Uruk had ever seen. They fought for hours. The earth shook and lightning flashed across the sky, as if the gods themselves were fighting for control of the world. Gilgamesh and Enkidu were

equal in strength and neither was winning. Then, suddenly, Gilgamesh stepped on a loose stone, stumbled, and fell over the edge of the wall.

It happened so quickly the people watching could not believe their eyes. To their amazement, Enkidu reached over the wall, grabbed Gilgamesh by the arm, and raised him to safety. Why? Enkidu had won. Why would he save someone who was trying to kill him?

Gilgamesh again stood on top of the wall facing Enkidu. All who watched held their breath. Gilgamesh took a step towards Enkidu, stopped, opened his arms, and embraced him. The king finally understood what it was to be human. He was no longer alone. He had found a friend.

The celebrations went on for days. Shamhat was chosen to lead the biggest parade that had ever taken place in Uruk. Gilgamesh and Enkidu, now brothers, watched and waved from atop the great wall.

Gilgamesh ordered work on the wall stopped forever. Fathers and mothers were reunited and danced with their children in the streets. Gilgamesh invited everyone to a great feast.

A new peace settled over Uruk. On quiet evenings, Shamhat liked to go out on the river with Enkidu and listen while he and Gilgamesh planned how they might make the city a happier place. Then she would play her harp and sing for them, proud that she had brought them together. As her voice floated across the water, the people of Uruk paused to listen. And they were grateful.

The Story of Gilgamesh

The story of the god-man Gilgamesh is one of the oldest stories in the world; it was inscribed onto clay tablets over 5000 years ago in Mesopotamia (where Iraq and Syria are today). There are many versions of the story, but the first people who told it were called Sumerians, and Gilgamesh was once their king. The people who lived in Mesopotamia discovered many things: irrigation, the wheel, the first codes of law, the 60-minute hour, and, most important, writing. Without writing, the epic of Gilgamesh would certainly have been lost. The Sumerians, and later other Mesopotamians such as the Akkadians, Babylonians, and Assyrians wrote the story in cuneiform, the first script in the world.

Mesopotamia means "the land between the rivers." On a map, one can see two rivers in Iraq: the Tigris and Euphrates. In between these rivers the land was very fertile and allowed for farming. When the ancient peoples started farming these lands over 8000 years ago, the extra food they produced eventually allowed others to build towns and then cities with names like Nippur, Ur, Lagash, and Uruk—the setting for the epic of Gilgamesh. The cities became the world's first civilization. Today, because the rivers have changed their course, the land around Uruk is almost entirely a desert, making it hard to believe that it was once covered with farmers' fields, trees, and great cities. One can still see the ruins of the wall built by Gilgamesh and the remains of other ancient cities.

Over time other peoples in Mesopotamia told versions of the Gilgamesh legend in places like Akkad, Babylonia, and Assyria. Later, parts of the story would make their way into the myths of Egypt, Greece, Persia, and even of the Celts in what are now the British Isles. Some of the stories in the Old Testament are said to share similar origins to the epic of Gilgamesh. Mesopotamia is believed to be the setting for the Garden of Eden and the birthplace of Abraham.

Clay tablets were first found in the earth of Iraq and Syria by French and British archaeologists in the 19th century. They brought the tablets home with them, and others translated cuneiform writing later in the century. Today these tablets continue to be found and can be seen in many museums, but those containing the Gilgamesh story are rare. The collections in London, Paris, and Philadelphia are especially famous.

ABOUT THE AUTHOR LUDMILA ZEMAN

Ludmila Zeman was born in Czechoslovakia. She is the daughter of Karel Zeman, a world renowned filmmaker. She became head designer for his films. Ludmila emigrated to Canada in 1984 with her husband and their two children. They have since taught film design at the Emily Carr College of Art in Vancouver and created films for Sesame Street and the National Film Board of Canada. Ludmila has also published a number of children's books. In 1988, Ludmila and her family became Canadian citizens.

The People Could Fly

by Virginia Hamilton
Illustrated by Anouk Pérousse-Bell

They say the people could fly. Say that long ago in Africa, some of the people knew magic. And they would walk up on the air like climbin up on a gate. And they flew like blackbirds over the fields. Black, shiny wings flappin against the blue up there.

Then, many of the people were captured for slavery. The ones that could fly shed their wings. They couldn't take their wings across the water on the slave ships. Too crowded, don't you know.

The folks were full of misery, then. Got sick with the up and down of the sea. So they forgot about flyin when they could no longer breathe the sweet scent of Africa.

Say the people who could fly kept their power, although they shed their wings. They kept their secret magic in the land of slavery. They looked the same as the other people from Africa who had been coming over, who had dark skin. Say you couldn't tell anymore one who could fly from one who couldn't.

One such who could was an old man, call him Toby. And standin tall, yet afraid, was a young woman who once had wings. Call her Sarah. Now Sarah carried a babe tied to her back. She trembled to be so hard worked and scorned.

The slaves labored in the fields from sunup to sundown. The owner of the slaves callin himself their Master. Say he was a hard lump of clay. A hard, glinty coal. A hard rock pile, wouldn't be moved. His Overseer on horseback pointed out the slaves who were slowin down. So the one called Driver cracked his whip over the slow ones to make them move faster. That whip was a slice-open cut of pain. So they did move faster. Had to.

Sarah hoed and chopped the row as the babe on her back slept.

Say the child grew hungry. That babe started up bawling too loud. Sarah couldn't stop to feed it. Couldn't stop to soothe and quiet it down. She let it cry. She didn't want to. She had no heart to croon to it.

"Keep that thing quiet," called the Overseer. He pointed his finger at the babe. The woman scrunched low. The Driver cracked his whip across the babe anyhow. The babe hollered like any hurt child, and the woman fell to the earth.

The old man that was there, Toby, came and helped her to her feet.

"I must go soon," she told him.

"Soon," he said.

Sarah couldn't stand up straight any longer. She was too weak. The sun burned her face. The babe cried and cried, "Pity me, oh, pity me," say it sounded like. Sarah was so sad and starvin, she sat down in the row.

"Get up, you black cow," called the Overseer. He pointed his hand, and the Driver's whip snarled around Sarah's legs. Her sack dress tore into rags. Her legs bled onto the earth. She couldn't get up.

Toby was there where there was no one to help her and the babe.

"Now, before it's too late," panted Sarah. "Now, Father!"

"Yes, Daughter, the time is come," Toby answered. "Go, as you know how to go!"

He raised his arms, holding them out to her. *"Kum . . . yali, kum buba tambe,"* and more magic words, said so quickly, they sounded like whispers and sighs.

The young woman lifted one foot on the air. Then the other. She flew clumsily at first, with the child now held tightly in her arms. Then she felt the magic, the African mystery. Say she rose just as free as a bird. As light as a feather.

The Overseer rode after her, hollerin. Sarah flew over the fences. She flew over the woods. Tall trees could not snag her. Nor could the Overseer.

She flew like an eagle now, until she was gone from sight. No one dared speak about it. Couldn't believe it. But it was, because they that was there saw that it was.

Say the next day was dead hot in the fields. A young man slave fell from the heat. The Driver come and whipped him. Toby come over and spoke words to the fallen one. The words of ancient Africa once heard are never remembered completely. The young man forgot them as soon as he heard them. They went way inside him. He got up and rolled over on the air. He rode it awhile. And he flew away.

Another and another fell from the heat. Toby was there. He cried out to the fallen and reached his arms out to them. *"Kum kunka yali, kum . . . tambe!"* Whispers and sighs. And they too

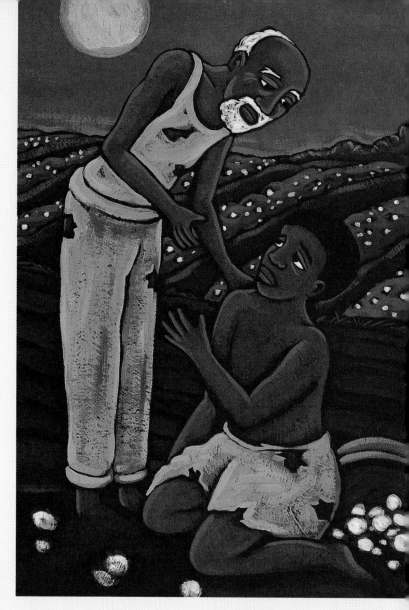

rose on the air. They rode the hot breezes. The ones flyin were black and shinin sticks, wheelin above the head of the Overseer. They crossed the rows, the fields, the fences, the streams, and were away.

"Seize the old man!" cried the Overseer. "I heard him say the magic *words*. Seize him!"

The one callin himself Master come runnin. The Driver got his whip ready to curl around old Toby and tie him up. The slaveowner took his hip gun from its place. He meant to kill old, black Toby.

But Toby just laughed. Say he threw back his head and said, "Hee, hee! Don't you know who I am? Don't you know some of us in this field?" He said it to their faces. "We are ones who fly!"

And he sighed the ancient words that were a dark promise. He said them all around to the others in the field under the whip, ". . . *buba yali . . . buba tambe. . . .*"

There was a great outcryin. The bent backs straighted up. Old and young who were called slaves and could fly joined hands. Say like they would ring-sing. But they didn't shuffle in a circle. They didn't sing. They rose on the air. They flew in a flock that was black against the heavenly blue. Black crows or black shadows. It didn't matter, they went so high. Way above the plantation, way over the slavery land. Say they flew away to *Free-dom*.

And the old man, old Toby, flew behind them, takin care of them. He wasn't cryin. He wasn't laughin. He was the seer. His gaze fell on the plantation where the slaves who could not fly waited.

"Take us with you!" Their looks spoke it but they were afraid to shout it. Toby couldn't take them with him. Hadn't the time to teach them to fly. They must wait for a chance to run.

"Goodie-bye!" The old man called Toby spoke to them, poor souls! And he was flyin gone.

So they say. The Overseer told it. The one called Master said it was a lie, a trick of the light. The Driver kept his mouth shut.

The slaves who could not fly told about the people who could fly to their children. When they were free. When they sat close before the fire in the free land, they told it. They did so love firelight and *Free-dom*, and tellin.

They say that the children of the ones who could not fly told their children. And now, me, I have told it to you.

The People Could Fly is one of the most extraordinary, moving tales in black folklore. It almost makes us believe that the people could fly. There are numerous separate accounts of flying Africans and slaves in the black folktale literature. Such accounts are often combined with tales of slaves disappearing. A plausible explanation might be the slaves running away from slavery, slipping away while in the fields or under cover of darkness. In code language murmured from one slave to another, "Come fly away!" might have been the words used. Another explanation is the wish-fulfilment motif.

The magic hoe variant is often combined with the flying-African tale. A magic hoe is left still hoeing in an empty field after all the slaves have flown away. Magic with the hoe and other farm tools, and the power of disappearing are often attributed to Gullah (Angolan) African slaves. Angolan slaves were thought by other slaves to have exceptional powers.

The People Could Fly is a detailed fantasy tale of suffering, of magic power exerted against the so-called Master and his underlings. Finally, it is a powerful testament to the millions of slaves who never had the opportunity to "fly" away. They remained slaves, as did their children. *The People Could Fly* was first told and retold by those who had only their imaginations to set them free.

ABOUT THE AUTHOR   VIRGINIA HAMILTON

Virginia Hamilton was born and raised in Ohio. Her mother's family had lived there since the late 1850s when Virginia's grandfather escaped from slavery on the Underground Railroad. Virginia is one of today's most honored writers for children and young adults. She has won many major awards, including the Coretta Scott King Award for *The People Could Fly*. She says: "There is no clear way to explain how it is that I have never ceased having new ideas for books nor the desire to work so intensely at writing them. . . . It is what I do. I will continue to explore the known, the remembered, and the imagined . . . of which every story is made..." Ms. Hamilton and her husband, poet Arnold Adoff, have two children and live in Yellow Springs, Ohio.

Gawain and the Lady Ragnell

by Ethel Johnston Phelps
Illustrated by Florentina

Long ago, in the days of King Arthur, the finest knight in all Britain was the king's nephew, Gawain. He was, by reputation, the bravest in battle, the wisest, the most courteous, the most compassionate, and the most loyal to his king.

One day in late summer, Gawain was with Arthur and the knights of the court at Carlisle in the north. The King returned from the day's hunting looking so pale and shaken that Gawain followed him at once to his chamber.

"What has happened, my lord?" asked Gawain with concern.

Arthur sat down heavily. "I had a very strange encounter in Inglewood forest . . . I hardly know what to make of it." And he related to Gawain what had occurred.

"Today I hunted a great white stag," said Arthur. "The stag at last escaped me and I was alone, some distance from my men. Suddenly a tall, powerful man appeared before me with sword upraised."

"And you were unarmed!"

"Yes. I had only my bow and a dagger in my belt. He threatened to kill me," Arthur went on. "And he swung his sword as though he meant to cut me down on the spot! Then he laughed horribly and said he would give me one chance to save my life."

"Who was this man?" cried Gawain. "Why should he want to kill you?"

"He said his name was Sir Gromer, and he sought revenge for the loss of his northern lands."

"A chieftain from the north!" exclaimed Gawain. "But what is this one chance he spoke of?"

"I gave him my word I would meet him one year from today, unarmed, at the same spot, with the answer to a question!" said Arthur.

Gawain started to laugh, but stopped at once when he saw Arthur's face. "A question! Is it a riddle? And one year to find the answer? That should not be hard!"

"If I can bring him the true answer to the question, 'What is it that women most desire, above all else?' my life will be spared." Arthur scowled. "He is sure I will fail. It must be a foolish riddle that no one can answer."

"My lord, we have one year to search the kingdom for answers," said Gawain confidently. "I will help you. Surely one of the answers will be the right one."

"No doubt you are right—someone will know the answer." Arthur looked more cheerful. "The man is mad, but a chieftain will keep his word."

For the next twelve months, Arthur and Gawain asked the question from one corner of the kingdom to the other. Then at last the appointed day drew near. Although they had many answers, Arthur was worried.

"With so many answers to choose from, how do we know which is the right one?" he asked in despair. "Not one of them has the ring of truth."

A few days before he was to meet Sir Gromer, Arthur rode out alone through the golden gorse and purple heather. The track led upward toward a grove of great oaks. Arthur, deep in thought, did not look up until he reached the edge of the oak wood. When he raised his head, he pulled up suddenly in astonishment.

Before him was a grotesque woman. She was almost as wide as she was high, her skin was mottled green, and spikes of weedlike hair covered her head. Her face seemed more animal than human.

The woman's eyes met Arthur's fearlessly. "You are Arthur the king," she said in a harsh, croaking voice. "In two days time, you must meet Sir Gromer with the answer to a question."

Arthur turned cold with fear. He stammered, "Yes . . . yes . . . that is true. Who are you? How did you know of this?"

"I am the lady Ragnell. Sir Gromer is my stepbrother. You haven't found the true answer, have you?"

"I have many answers," Arthur replied curtly. "I do not see how my business concerns you." He gathered up the reins, eager to be gone.

"You do not have the right answer." Her certainty filled him with a sense of doom. The harsh voice went on, "But I know the answer to Sir Gromer's question."

Arthur turned back in hope and disbelief. "You do? Tell me the true answer to his question, and I will give you a large bag of gold."

"I have no use for gold," she said coldly.

"Nonsense, my good woman. With gold you can buy anything you want!" He hesitated a moment, for the huge, grotesque face with the cool, steady eyes unnerved him. He went on hurriedly, "What is it you want? Jewellery? Land? Whatever you want I will pay you—that is, if you truly have the right answer."

"I know the answer. I promise you that!" She paused. "What I demand in return is that the knight Gawain become my husband."

There was a moment of shocked silence. Then Arthur cried, "Impossible! You ask the impossible, woman!"

She shrugged and turned to leave.

"Wait, wait a moment!" Rage and panic overwhelmed him, but he tried to speak reasonably.

"I offer you gold, land, jewels. I cannot give you my nephew. He is his own man. He is not mine to give!"

"I did not ask you to *give* me the knight Gawain," she rebuked him. "If Gawain himself agrees to marry me, I will give you the answer. Those are my terms."

"Impossible!" he sputtered. "I could not bring him such a proposal."

"If you should change your mind, I will be here tomorrow," said she, and disappeared into the oak woods.

Shaken from the weird encounter, Arthur rode homeward at a slow pace.

"Save my own life at Gawain's expense? Never!" he thought. "Loathsome woman! I could not even speak of it to Gawain."

But the afternoon air was soft and sweet with birdsong, and the fateful meeting with Sir Gromer weighed on him heavily. He was torn by the terrible choice facing him.

Gawain rode out from the castle to meet the king. Seeing Arthur's pale, strained face, he exclaimed, "My lord! Are you ill? What has happened?"

"Nothing . . . nothing at all." But he could not keep silent long. "The colossal impudence of the woman! A monster, that's what she is! That creature, daring to give me terms!"

"Calm yourself, uncle," Gawain said patiently. "What woman? Terms for what?"

Arthur sighed. "She knows the answer to the question. I didn't intend to tell you."

"Why not? Surely that's good news! What is the answer?"

"She will not tell me until her terms are met," said the king heavily. "But I assure you, I refuse to consider her proposal!"

Gawain smiled. "You talk in riddles yourself, uncle. Who is this woman who claims to know the answer? What is her proposal?"

Seeing Gawain's smiling, expectant face, Arthur at first could not speak. Then, with his eyes averted, the king told Gawain the whole story, leaving out no detail.

"The lady Ragnell is Sir Gromer's stepsister? Yes, I think she would know the right answer," Gawain said thoughtfully. "How fortunate that I will be able to save your life!"

"No! I will not let you sacrifice yourself!" Arthur cried.

"It is my choice and my decision," Gawain answered. "I will return with you tomorrow and agree to the marriage—on condition that the answer she supplies is the right one to save your life."

Early the following day, Gawain rode out with Arthur. But not even meeting the loathsome lady face to face could shake his resolve. Her proposal was accepted.

Gawain bowed courteously. "If on the morrow your answer saves the king's life, we will be wed."

On the fateful morning, Gawain watched the king stow a parchment in his saddlebag. "I'll try all these answers first," said Arthur.

They rode together for the first part of the journey. Then Arthur, unarmed as agreed, rode on alone to Inglewood to meet Sir Gromer.

The tall, powerful chieftain was waiting, his broadsword glinting in the sun.

Arthur read off one answer, then another, and another. Sir Gromer shook his head in satisfaction.

"No, you have not the right answer!" he said raising his sword high. "You've failed, and now—"

"Wait!" Arthur cried. "I have one more answer. What a woman desires above all else is the power of sovereignty—the right to exercise her own will."

The man dropped his sword. "You did not find that answer by yourself!" he shouted. "My stepsister, Ragnell, gave it to you. Bold, interfering hussy! I'll run her through with my sword . . . I'll lop off her head . . ." Turning, he plunged into the forest.

Arthur rode back to where Gawain waited with the monstrous Ragnell. They returned to the castle in silence. Only the grotesque Lady Ragnell seemed in good spirits.

The news spread quickly throughout the castle. Gawain, the finest knight in the land, was to marry this monstrous creature! Some tittered and laughed at the spectacle; others said the lady Ragnell must possess very great lands and estates; but mostly there was stunned silence.

Arthur took his nephew aside nervously. "Must you go through with it at once? A postponement perhaps?"

Gawain looked at him steadily. "I gave my promise, my lord. The lady Ragnell's answer saved your life. Would you have me—"

"Your loyalty makes me ashamed! Of course you cannot break your word." And Arthur turned away.

The marriage took place in the abbey. Afterward, with Gawain and the lady Ragnell sitting at the high dais table beside the king and queen, the strange wedding feast began.

"She takes the space of two women on the chair," muttered the knight Gareth. "Poor Gawain!"

"I would not marry such a creature for all the land in Christendom!" answered his companion.

An uneasy silence settled on the hall. Only the monstrous Lady Ragnell displayed good spirits and good appetite. Throughout the long day and evening, Gawain remained pleasant and courteous. In no way did his manner toward his strange bride show other than kind attention.

The wedding feast drew to a close. Gawain and his bride were conducted to their chamber and were at last alone.

The lady Ragnell gazed at her husband thoughtfully.

"You have kept your promise well and faithfully," she observed.

Gawain inclined his head. "I could not do less, my lady."

"You've shown neither revulsion nor pity," she said. After a pause she went on, "Come now, we are wedded! I am waiting to be kissed."

Gawain went to her at once and kissed her. When he stepped back, there stood before him a slender young woman with grey eyes and a serene, smiling face.

His scalp tingled in shock. "What manner of enchantment is this?" he cried hoarsely.

"Do you prefer me in this form?" she smiled and turned slowly in a full circle.

But Gawain backed away warily. "I . . . yes . . . of course . . . but . . . I don't understand . . ." For this sudden evidence of enchantment, with its unknown powers, made him confused and uneasy.

"My stepbrother, Sir Gromer, had always hated me," said the lady Ragnell. "Unfortunately, through his mother, he has a knowledge of enchantment, and so he changed me into a monstrous creature. He said I must live in that shape until I could persuade the greatest knight in Britain to willingly choose me for his bride. He said it would be an impossible condition to meet!"

"Why did he hate you so cruelly?"

Her lips curled in amusement. "He thought me bold and unwomanly because I defied him. I refused his commands both for my property and my person."

Gawain said with admiration, "You won the 'impossible' condition he set, and now his enchantment is broken!"

"Only in part." Her clear grey eyes held his. "You have a choice, my dear Gawain, which way I will be. Would you have me in this, my own shape, at night and my former ugly shape by day? Or would you have me grotesque at night in our chamber, and my own shape in the castle by day? Think carefully before you choose."

Gawain was silent only a moment. He knelt before her and touched her hand.

"It is a choice I cannot make, my dear Ragnell. It concerns you. Whatever you choose to be—fair by day or fair by night—I will willingly abide by it."

Ragnell released a long, deep breath. The radiance in her face overwhelmed him.

"You have answered well, dearest Gawain, for your answer has broken Gromer's enchantment completely. The last condition he set has been met! For he said that if, after marriage to the greatest knight in Britain, my husband freely gave me the power of choice, the power to exercise my own free will, the wicked enchantment would be broken forever."

Thus, in wonder and in joy, began the marriage of Gawain and the lady Ragnell.

ABOUT THE AUTHOR — ETHEL JOHNSTON PHELPS

Ethel Johnston Phelps wrote plays for stage and radio. As well, she wrote collections of folk and fairytales. Ethel lived in Rockville Centre, New York, with her husband and three sons.

L'Anse aux Meadows *from an etching by David Blackwood*

The Legend of Vinland

by Joan Horwood

Leif put to sea, and was at sea a long time, and lighted on those lands whose existence he had not so much as dreamt of before. There were wheatfields growing wild there and grown (grape) vines. There were also those trees which are called maple, and they fetched away with them samples of all these things—some trees so big that they were used in housebuilding. . . . Leif reached land in Eiriksfjord (Greenland) and then went home to Brattahlid, where they all welcomed him with open arms. . . .

— from Eirik the Red

The Legend of Vinland

The early accounts of Viking voyages to North America come to us from the sagas—ancient Scandinavian stories that were told by word of mouth for many years, and later written down for future generations to read. (The earliest written version of the sagas dates back to the twelfth century.) We can trace the beginning of the Vikings movement westward toward North America by reading in the sagas of the sea voyages of Eirik the Red and Bjarni Herjolfsson.

Eirik the Red

Eirik the Red was a Norwegian-born settler in Iceland. In about 982, because he was involved in a feud that resulted in the death of two sons of a nobleman, the local assembly sentenced him to exile from Iceland for three years. Setting sail westward in a knarr, he arrived in a land that he would later name "Greenland." At the end of his banishment, he returned to Iceland and mounted an expedition to colonize the new land.

In the year 986, a fleet of twenty-five ocean-going Viking ships under Eirik's command, departed from Iceland for Eiriksfjord, Greenland. It was a rough voyage, with only fourteen ships completing the journey. The others were shipwrecked or forced to turn back to Iceland. The newcomers settled in the new land, constructing dwellings from stones and turf. The men fished and hunted while the women looked after the cattle and occupied

Replica of Viking boat at L'Anse aux Meadows

themselves with domestic chores.

About ten years later, a second settlement was established further up the coast to the northwest. These Norse colonies in Greenland would continue to exist for another 500 years.

Eirik the Red had brought his family with him from Iceland. He had four children—Leif, Thorstein, Thorvald, and Freydis. Leif Eiriksson grew up in Greenland and often entertained thoughts of exploration and adventure, having heard stories of them as a boy. He was particularly interested in the story told of a strange new country to the west that had been sighted by Bjarni Herjolfsson.

Bjarni Herjolfsson

In the summer of 986, the same year that Eirik the Red settled in Greenland, Bjarni Herjolfsson sailed from Iceland to spend the winter with his father in Greenland. The weather turned bad and fog shrouded the ocean, causing him to lose his direction. His ship drifted to the southwest, carried by the wind and the current. When the weather finally cleared a day later, he saw a coastline; it was low-lying and covered with trees. He knew this was not Greenland because it did not have the same great fiords, distant mountains, and meadows previously described to him.

Bjarni turned toward the north and sailed for two days, past more flat land covered with trees. He

carried on for three more days until he came to a third land; this one was covered with mountains and glaciers.

Without landing anywhere, he turned back, setting a northeasterly course and holding it for four more days. He finally reached his father's home in Greenland. On his arrival, Bjarni told of his accidental discovery of new lands.

Thrilling as the story of these mysterious territories was, several years would pass before the Vikings were ready to explore them.

Leif Eiriksson Reaches the New Land

It was fifteen years later that Eirik the Red's son, Leif Eiriksson, went in search of the new land Bjarni Herjolfsson had described. He bought Bjarni's ship and took on some of the same crew. The members of Leif's crew would have been dressed in woollen trousers and shirts to keep them warm on sea voyages. A cloak was also worn in cold climates to shield them from the wind. It was fastened at the shoulder to enable a quick withdrawal of the sword from the sheath worn beneath. Setting a westerly course, they sailed from Greenland into the uncharted sea ahead of them.

A few days later, Leif came to a barren land, a place of flat stones with glaciers etched against the sky. This may have been the south shore of Baffin Island. He called it Helluland, which meant "land of flat stones."

Replica sod buildings at L'Anse aux Meadows

He left this forbidding country and sailed on with his thirty-five companions until he came to another place. It was pleasant, with low, forest-clad slopes, the land falling gently to white sandy beaches. He called it Markland—"land of woods." This was probably coastal Labrador, which has a forty-eight-kilometre stretch of white sandy beaches along Cape Porcupine.

He then sailed in a southerly direction for two more days until he came to a place he called Vinland, a land of grassy meadows. Here Leif and his men carried their leather sleeping bags ashore and built temporary shelters. When they later decided to spend the winter there, they built "large houses."

The sagas also mention that one of Leif Eiriksson's crew, named Tyrker, became separated from his companions. When he returned to them, he told Leif that he had found grapes on grapevines. Leif sent his men out to cut wood and gather grapes to take back to Greenland. By reason of this story, people have believed for many years that Leif Eiriksson called his new home "Vinland" for the grapes which were discovered there on vines.

So began a series of expeditions to Vinland by Leif and other members of his family. His brother, Thorvald, was next to go and then his second brother, Thorstein, whose attempt failed. Even his half-sister, Freydis, later adventured to this new land. The sagas describing these early expeditions provide most of the information that is known about this first Viking colony on the North American continent.

The End of the Viking Era

Little is known about Viking expeditions to Vinland after the time of Freydis. Icelandic annals record only two further efforts: a twelfth century voyage by Eirik, Bishop of Greenland, "in search of Vinland," and a Greenland ship that reached Markland in 1347, but was driven off by storms to Iceland when it attempted to return home.

The Norse settlements in Greenland grew and flourished up to the thirteenth century. At its height of prosperity, the entire colony consisted of perhaps 4000 people, and had approximately 300 farms, 16 churches, 2 monasteries, and a bishop. However, by the end of the fifteenth century, the descendents of Eirik the Red and other Vikings seem to have left Greenland. It was reached by Martin Frobisher in 1578, who landed on the west coast. In 1721 Hans Egede, a Danish-Norwegian missionary, founded a settlement near Godthaab on the east coast of Greenland. Upon his arrival, he found only the ruins of old buildings.

The Viking era had gradually faded into history, but records of their explorations were found in the hands of several Icelandic families. Many of the sagas had been preserved for 300 or 400 years. In 1837, Carl C. Rafn, a Scandinavian scholar, acquired some of the ancient stories telling of early Viking settlements in Greenland and Vinland. The ruins in Greenland were easily found, but where was the location of Vinland? Thus began the search for Vinland.

ABOUT THE AUTHOR JOAN HORWOOD

Joan Horwood spent her entire life in Newfoundland where she wrote everything from history texts and novels to television scripts and children's plays. Most of her texts and novels were based on the history of Newfoundland. They include titles such as *The Great Halifax Explosion* and *William Epps Cormack: His Historic Walk Across Newfoundland in 1822*. Joan thoroughly researched all of her books both in Canada and, when necessary, overseas. Her goal was to write books that made history easy to read and entertaining.

Computer art by Timothy Benson

It's All Over

When I woke up, I was again in the camp infirmary. I sat up and looked around, trying to remember what happened. Then I remembered. The Gryphon Riders flying from the North, the giant cheers, the pain in my head. But what happened after that?

Just then the medic walked in and I quickly asked, "What happened? Is the war over? Did we win?"

The medic answered "Aye sir, we have won. The war is over and the knights have just captured the last Orcs. Just after the Gryphons came, you were hurt by an Orc. Luckily, you are safe. I was sent to give you a message that you have been promoted to leader of all the free peoples of the North. Congrats. Of course, you know you were promoted for pushing back the Orcs beyond the frontiers of our land, Southshore. You are a very brave man, General. I have also been told to tell you that the Gryphons have offered a treaty to the Alliance of Humans, Dwarfs, and Elves. Now we shall have a force to control the Orcs."

"Aye," I answered, "that will be my next task. Yes. . . to control the world of the Orcs. Southshore wasn't that hard, so I say we start on all of the world. Yes . . . " And I drifted off into dreams that for once in a long time, were peaceful. THE END.

by Gabe Stein
Grade 6

Dragon Fire

I walked through the bone filled caves
I had been training for this
for days and days,
A shield in one hand
a sword in the other
And bracing myself in many ways.

Then I heard a sound of falling rocks
(nothing but a small fox)
I smelled the fumes of smoke
I knew I was close
I gripped my sword nervously
and sweating from excitement
I looked around the corner
and there it was,
The ugliest beast I have ever seen
Its fangs were razor sharp
with eyes of glaring green.

It was the great Dragon King
what a hideous thing!
It turned around in a wink of an eye,

So I built up my courage and
ran at the beast
But it blew fire...

With my shield in front of me
I retreated until
the fire stopped in its track
I repeated my act, advanced
and thrust my sword with a flourish.

The great beast struggled
then gave up the fight.
I saw it rest in peace and knew
That was my destiny.

I walked out of the cave
thinking of the Dragon,
"He is no match for me, I'm the best
What foul beast or ogre will face me next?"

by Tyler Hammerstadt
Grade 7

Weeping Woods

A long time ago, a great myth was passed down. The myth was that if you were to go through Weeping Woods, you would be robbed of all you had. Many people told the story of how the trolls robbed them of their riches. Of course, nobody believed them.

About 5 kilometres away from Weeping Woods, there was a castle ruled by a great king. The king's subjects were very worried about the myth, so they asked the king to send his bravest knights to Weeping Woods. The king assured them that it was just a myth and sent the knights to prove it.

So, in one day, the knights travelled to Weeping Woods with five tonnes of gold coins and jewels. They stayed there overnight. The next morning they travelled back to the castle with their five tonnes of gold and jewels. One of the knights told the king that they had not been robbed. When the king asked to see his riches, the knights took the gold and jewels out of the sack. To their surprise, the gold and jewels had been switched with blocks of wood.

So, if you are near Weeping Woods, beware the trolls!

by Scott Russell
Age 10

I wrote about trolls because I am interested in them. I think they are unique little furry creatures that can sneak around without a trace.

Glossary

Abyssinia	an old name for the country of Ethiopia in northern Africa
addax	a rare African antelope with spiral horns
alicorn	the horn of a unicorn
bunyip	in Australian Aboriginal mythology, a swamp-dwelling creature with webbed feet and feathers
calabash	a kind of gourd; its dried skin can be used as a container
Chinese characters	the basic elements of Chinese writing
dais	a platform raised above floor level
eon	a very long period of time
fennec fox	a large-eared desert fox
Gabon viper	a poisonous snake native to Gabon in Africa
griffin	a mythical beast with head, wings, and forelegs of an eagle and the body, hind legs, and tail of a lion
jerboa	a desert rat that resembles a miniature kangaroo
kar-ka-dann	the fierce unicorn of Persian mythology
knarr	a type of Viking ship used for long voyages
legend	a story from the past that is widely accepted as being true or partly true
lore	facts and stories about a certain subject
manticore	a mythical beast with the head of a man, the body of a tiger or lion, and the feet and tail of a scorpion or dragon
myth	a traditional story about godlike beings
parapet	a low protective wall along the edge of a roof
saga	a prose narrative about heroic deeds, written and told in Iceland and Norway in the Middle Ages
sphinx	in Greek mythology, a beast with the head of a human, the body of a lion, and the wings of a bird; in Egyptian mythology, a beast with the head of a human and the body of a lion
stylus	a sharp pointed instrument used for writing or engraving
tree pangolin	a long-tailed anteater that spends most of its time in trees
yang	in Chinese mythology, the male force that affects human existence
yin	in Chinese mythology, the female force that affects human existence